Chocolate Fantasies

Oxmoor House®

ISBN: 0-8487-2939-0

Manufactured in the United States of America

CHOCOLATE FANTASIES

Cover: *Fudge Pie* (Page 67).

Contents

Introduction

Dark, rich chocolate is full of melt-in-your-mouth goodness. So what could be better than a collection of irresistible chocolate treats? From silky smooth chocolate mousse to towering chocolate cake, this sweet extravaganza is sure to be a valuable resource for lasting pleasure.

Real chocolate lovers will want to sample their way through the cookbook by starting with a mug of steaming hot chocolate accompanied by chocolate-glazed doughnuts or a wedge of chocolate cream pie. Our chocolate cakes and chocolate chip cookies will make your family and friends happy over and over again (don't be surprised if they ask for the recipes). Gift givers, knowing that chocolate candy can win the hearts of many, will delight in our luscious assortment of confections.

As an added bonus, there is an entire chapter devoted to sauces and frostings. Pick any of the rich fudge sauces and spoon them over ice cream or a slice of cake for a quick, delicious dessert. And layer cakes become showpieces with a generous spreading of our thick and creamy frostings.

We begin the book with a section of hints on how to cook with chocolate. You'll discover easy methods for melting chocolate plus simple explanations of the different types of chocolate and how they can be used interchangeably. Also included in this section are instructions for making chocolate garnishes—you'll find chocolate leaves and chocolate curls are easier to prepare than you might think.

All About Chocolate

TYPES OF CHOCOLATE

Unsweetened Chocolate: The basic chocolate from which all other products are made. It is molded into 1-ounce blocks and sold in 8-ounce packages. It may also be sold melted and packaged in envelopes.

Semisweet Chocolate: Unsweetened chocolate with sugar, extra cocoa butter, and flavorings added to give it a satiny gloss. It is molded into 1-ounce blocks and sold in 8-ounce packages or formed into chocolate chips.

Sweet Baking Chocolate (German Sweet Chocolate): Similar to semisweet chocolate, but has more sugar and is packaged in 4-ounce bars.

Milk Chocolate: Sweet chocolate with milk added. It is sold in various shapes and bars.

Almond Bark: An artificial chocolate made with vegetable fats instead of cocoa butter, with coloring and flavorings added. It is sold in 1½-pound packages or in blocks and round discs where candy supplies are sold.

Unsweetened Cocoa: A form of pure chocolate with most of the cocoa butter removed and ground into powder. It is sold in 8-ounce or 16-ounce cans.

Chocolate-Flavored Syrup: A combination of cocoa, corn syrup, and flavoring and is available in various sizes in jars, cans, or plastic containers.

CHOCOLATE SUBSTITUTIONS

We specify the type of chocolate we used in testing for each of the recipes. If you need to make substitutions, use the following information as a guide. However, for best results, always use the chocolate specified in each recipe.

To substitute for:

1 (1-ounce) square unsweetened chocolate—use 3 tablespoons unsweetened cocoa and 1 tablespoon shortening.

1 ounce semisweet chocolate—use 3 tablespoons semisweet chocolate chips or 1 (1-ounce) square unsweetened chocolate and 1 tablespoon sugar.

6-ounce package (1 cup) semisweet chocolate morsels—use 6 tablespoons unsweetened cocoa, ¼ cup sugar, and ¼ cup shortening.

4-ounce bar sweet baking chocolate—use ¼ cup unsweetened cocoa, ⅓ cup sugar, and 3 tablespoons shortening.

Note: When melted, semisweet chocolate morsels and semisweet chocolate squares can be used interchangeably.

HOW TO STORE CHOCOLATE

Store chocolate tightly wrapped or covered in a cool, dry place or in the refrigerator. If refrigerated, let it warm to room temperature before using.

Occasionally, there may be a slight graying or “bloom” on chocolate. This does not alter the quality or flavor and when used in a recipe, the chocolate will regain its color.

HOW TO MELT CHOCOLATE

Always melt chocolate with gentle heat because it scorches easily. If chocolate is to be melted alone, make certain that the container and utensils are absolutely dry; a tiny drop of moisture will cause the chocolate to become lumpy and stiff. If this should happen, stir in one teaspoon of vegetable shortening for each ounce of chocolate. Remember that unsweetened chocolate liquifies when melted, but semisweet and baking chocolate will hold their shapes until stirred. For faster melting, cut or chop chocolate into smaller pieces.

To melt chocolate, place it in a heavy saucepan over low heat and stir until melted. Or, place chocolate in top of a double boiler and melt over hot water, stirring until smooth.

To melt chocolate in a microwave oven, place a 1-ounce square in a 1-cup glass measure. Microwave, uncovered, at MEDIUM (50% power) for 1 to 2 minutes or until chocolate is almost melted. Stir until completely melted and smooth. Add 10 seconds for each additional ounce of chocolate.

To melt chocolate morsels in a microwave oven, place 1 cup chocolate morsels in a 2-cup glass measure. Microwave, uncovered, at MEDIUM (50% power) for 2 to 4 minutes or until morsels are glossy. Stir until smooth.

CHOCOLATE GARNISHES

Chocolate Leaves: Select non-poisonous leaves such as mint or rose leaves. Wash the leaves and pat dry with paper towels. Melt 1 or 2 (1-ounce) squares semisweet chocolate over hot water in a double boiler; let cool slightly. Using a small spatula, spread a thin layer of chocolate on the back of each leaf. Place leaves on a wax paper-lined cookie sheet, chocolate side up; freeze until chocolate is firm, about 10 minutes. Grasp leaf at stem end and carefully peel away from chocolate. Chill leaves until ready to use.

Chocolate Curls: Melt 4 (1-ounce) squares semisweet chocolate over hot water in a double boiler. Pour chocolate out into a wax paper-lined cookie sheet. Spread chocolate with a spatula into a 3-inch-wide strip. Smooth top with a spatula. Chill chocolate until it feels slightly tacky but not firm. (If too hard, curls will break; if too soft, chocolate will not curl.)

Gently pull a vegetable peeler across chocolate until curls form. Transfer curls to a tray by inserting a wooden pick in end of curl. Chill curls until ready to use.

Chocolate-Dipped Fruit: Make sure fruit is completely dry before dipping. Melt 4 (1-ounce) squares semisweet chocolate over hot water in a double boiler; transfer to a small bowl, and let cool slightly. Grasp fruit by stem and dip in chocolate, turning to coat the bottom of the fruit. Allow excess to drip back into bowl. Lay fruit on side on a wax paper-lined cookie sheet. Allow fruit to stand at room temperature until chocolate hardens or place in refrigerator about 10 minutes. Don't store coated fruit in refrigerator; the chocolate coating will sweat when returned to room temperature and will lose its sheen.

Chocolate Cutouts: Melt 6 (1-ounce) squares semisweet chocolate over hot water in a double boiler; cool slightly. Line a cookie sheet with aluminum foil; pour the chocolate onto the cookie sheet, and gently shake it until chocolate is smooth and level and about ⅛-inch thick. Let stand until partially set. Press a cookie cutter half-way through the chocolate to outline shapes. Remove the cutter, and let stand until chocolate is firm. When hard, reposition the cutter over the outlines, and press down to cut smoothly. Lift the cutter up, and remove the cutout by gently pressing through the cutter with a small wooden utensil (fingers will leave prints on chocolate).

Grated Chocolate: You can grate unsweetened, semisweet, or milk chocolate to sprinkle on top of pies, etc. It's easiest done in a food processor, but you can grate it by hand. When grating by hand, hold chocolate with a paper towel or wax paper so heat from your hand will not soften or melt the chocolate.

Beverages

OLD-FASHIONED HOT CHOCOLATE

2 (1-ounce) squares unsweetened chocolate
1⅓ cups boiling water
1 quart milk
⅓ cup sugar
Pinch of salt
½ teaspoon vanilla extract
Marshmallows or whipped cream (optional)

Place chocolate in top of a double boiler; bring water to a boil. Reduce heat to low; cook until chocolate melts. Gradually add 1⅓ cups boiling water, stirring constantly. Remove from heat; set aside.

Heat milk in a heavy saucepan just until thoroughly heated (do not boil). Stir in sugar and salt; add chocolate mixture, stirring well. Cook over low heat, stirring occasionally. Remove from heat; stir in vanilla. Top with marshmallows or whipped cream, if desired. Serve immediately. Yield: 6 cups.

QUICK INDIVIDUAL HOT COCOA

2 teaspoons cocoa
2 teaspoons sugar
¼ cup water
¾ cup milk
Miniature marshmallows (optional)

Combine first 3 ingredients in a small saucepan, and bring to a boil. Boil 3 minutes, stirring constantly. Stir in milk; heat just until thoroughly heated (do not boil). Top with marshmallows, if desired. Serve immediately. Yield: 1 cup.

SPECIAL HOT CHOCOLATE

2 cups milk
½ cup candy-coated chocolate pieces
2 tablespoons molasses
¼ teaspoon ground ginger
Whipped cream

Heat milk in a heavy saucepan just until thoroughly heated (do not boil). Combine candy-coated chocolate, molasses, and ginger in container of an electric blender; add milk. Process at high speed about 1 minute or until smooth. Top with whipped cream. Serve immediately. Yield: about 2½ cups.

SPICED HOT CHOCOLATE

6 cups milk
½ cup sugar
3 (1-ounce) squares unsweetened chocolate, cut into small pieces
1 teaspoon ground cinnamon
¼ teaspoon salt
2 eggs, beaten
2 teaspoons vanilla extract

Combine first 5 ingredients in a large saucepan, mixing well; cook over medium heat, stirring constantly, until chocolate melts. Gradually stir about one-fourth of hot mixture into eggs; add to remaining hot mixture. Cook over low heat 2 to 3 minutes, stirring constantly. Remove from heat; add vanilla, and beat at medium speed of an electric mixer until frothy. Serve immediately. Yield: 6 cups.

INSTANT COCOA-COFFEE

1 cup instant cocoa mix
⅓ cup instant coffee granules
4 cups boiling water
Whipped cream

Combine cocoa mix, instant coffee, and boiling water; stir until coffee granules completely dissolve.

Garnish each serving with whipped cream. Serve immediately. Yield: 4 cups.

FAVORITE HOT CHOCOLATE

1½ cups sugar
½ cup cocoa
¾ teaspoon salt
5 cups water
1 (12-ounce) can evaporated milk
2 cups milk
Marshmallows (optional)

Combine sugar, cocoa, and salt in a large Dutch oven; mix well. Slowly stir in water; bring to a boil. Add milk; cook just until thoroughly heated (do not boil).

Place marshmallows in individual cups, if desired; fill cups with hot chocolate. Serve immediately. Yield: 10 cups.

CHOCOLATE CASTLE CAPPUCCINO

3 cups cold water
¼ cup finely ground French roast coffee
About ½ cup chocolate syrup
1 cup whipping cream
Grated chocolate
5 (4-inch) sticks cinnamon

Pour water into reservoir of espresso-cappuccino maker; add coffee to filter. Brew espresso according to manufacturer's instructions, and fill coffee cups one-third full. Add 1 tablespoon plus 1 teaspoon chocolate syrup to each cup of espresso, stirring well.

Pour whipping cream into a small, deep, chilled metal or ceramic pitcher. Place steam nozzle of cappuccino maker in the bottom of the pitcher. Slowly release steam completely. Lower pitcher until end of nozzle is just below surface of cream. Continue to steam until whipping cream foams and doubles in volume. Pour foamed whipping cream over brewed espresso, filling cups full. Sprinkle each serving with grated chocolate. Place a cinnamon stick in each cup. Serve immediately. Yield: 5 cups.

Note: If steamed cream does not become frothy and double in volume, pour over espresso and stir to mix before serving.

CHOCOLATE MALT

1 cup milk
1 tablespoon plus 2 teaspoons chocolate malt
1½ tablespoons powdered chocolate flavoring for milk
1 quart vanilla ice cream, softened

Combine all ingredients in container of an electric blender; process until smooth. Pour into individual glasses. Serve immediately. Yield: 4 cups.

PLANTATION COFFEE PUNCH

1 quart chocolate milk
½ gallon chocolate, coffee, or vanilla ice cream, cubed and softened
2 quarts strong coffee, chilled
Whipped cream
Ground nutmeg

Combine first 3 ingredients in a punch bowl; stir until ice cream melts. Garnish with dollops of whipped cream and sprinkle with nutmeg. Yield: 20 cups.

FRENCH CHOCOLATE MILK

⅓ cup semisweet chocolate morsels
¼ cup light corn syrup
3 tablespoons water
½ teaspoon vanilla extract
1 cup whipping cream
1 quart milk, scalded

Combine chocolate morsels, corn syrup, and water in a small heavy saucepan; cook over low heat, stirring constantly, until chocolate is melted and mixture is smooth. Stir in vanilla. Cover and chill 30 to 45 minutes, stirring occasionally.

Gradually add chocolate mixture to whipping cream, beating with an electric mixer until stiff peaks form. Chill.

To serve, place ½ cup chocolate cream in each cup. Add milk, stirring well. Yield: about 7 cups.

CHOCOLATE-MINT SMOOTHIE

2 cups milk, divided
¼ cup instant cocoa mix
½ teaspoon vanilla extract
⅛ teaspoon peppermint extract
1 pint vanilla ice cream

Heat ½ cup milk in a heavy saucepan just until thoroughly heated (do not boil). Combine hot milk and cocoa mix in container of an electric blender; process until smooth. Add remaining 1½ cups milk, vanilla, and peppermint; blend well. Add ice cream, and process until mixture is smooth. Serve immediately. Yield: 4 cups.

CHOCOLATE ALEXANDERS

1 quart skim milk
2 tablespoons instant coffee powder
¼ cup chocolate syrup
½ teaspoon vanilla extract
½ to 1 teaspoon brandy extract
Frozen whipped topping, thawed
Grated chocolate (optional)

Combine first 3 ingredients in a heavy saucepan; cook over medium heat, stirring frequently, just until thoroughly heated (do not boil). Stir in flavorings. Ladle into mugs, and garnish with whipped topping. Sprinkle with chocolate, if desired. Serve immediately. Yield: 4 cups.

MEXICAN COFFEE

24 cups hot coffee
1 (16-ounce) can chocolate syrup
1 cup Kahlúa or other coffee-flavored liqueur
½ teaspoon ground cinnamon
Whipped cream

Combine coffee, chocolate syrup, Kahlúa, and cinnamon in a large container; stir well. Top each serving with a dollop of whipped cream. Serve immediately. Yield: 25 cups.

Note: Mexican Coffee may also be served cold with a scoop of ice cream.

VIENNESE CHOCOLATE

1 (6-ounce) package semisweet chocolate morsels
½ cup sugar
1 teaspoon grated orange rind
⅓ cup orange juice
½ teaspoon ground cinnamon
1 cup whipping cream, whipped
Hot milk
Cointreau or other orange-flavored liqueur (optional)
Cinnamon sticks

Combine first 5 ingredients in a heavy saucepan. Cook over low heat, stirring constantly, until smooth. Remove from heat, and cool to lukewarm. Fold whipped cream into chocolate mixture; cover and refrigerate up to 1 week.

To serve, spoon 2 tablespoons chocolate mixture into each cup; add ⅔ cup hot milk and 1 ounce Cointreau, if desired, stirring until blended. Serve each with a cinnamon stick stirrer. Yield: enough to make about 20 cups.

FRENCH HOT CHOCOLATE

4 (1-ounce) squares unsweetened chocolate
¼ cup water
4 cups milk
½ cup half-and-half
½ cup sugar
2 tablespoons rum
¼ teaspoon salt
¼ teaspoon ground mace
⅛ teaspoon ground allspice
1 teaspoon vanilla extract
½ teaspoon almond extract
⅛ teaspoon ground nutmeg
½ cup whipping cream, whipped

Combine chocolate and water in a heavy saucepan; cook over low heat, stirring until chocolate melts. Gradually add milk, half-and-half, sugar, rum, salt, mace, and allspice. Cook over medium heat, stirring with a wire whisk, until mixture is hot. Stir in flavorings. Pour into cups. Fold nutmeg into whipped cream. Top each cup with whipped cream. Yield: 5 cups.

Breads

CHOCOLATE DOUGHNUTS

2 eggs
1¼ cups sugar
¼ cup vegetable oil
1 teaspoon vanilla extract
4 cups all-purpose flour
⅓ cup cocoa
1 tablespoon plus 1 teaspoon baking powder
1 teaspoon ground cinnamon
¾ teaspoon salt
¼ teaspoon baking soda
¾ cup buttermilk
Vegetable oil
Glaze (recipe follows)

Beat eggs at medium speed of an electric mixer until frothy. Gradually add sugar, beating until thick and lemon-colored; stir in ¼ cup vegetable oil and vanilla.

Combine the next 6 ingredients and add to egg mixture alternately with buttermilk, beginning and ending with flour mixture. Cover dough; chill several hours.

Divide dough in half. Working with one portion at a time, place dough on a lightly floured surface; roll out to ½-inch thickness. Cut dough with a floured 2½-inch doughnut cutter.

Heat 2 to 3 inches of oil to 375°; drop in 4 or 5 doughnuts at a time. Cook about 1 minute or until golden on one side; turn and cook other side about 1 minute. Drain well on paper towels. Dip each doughnut in glaze; cool on wax paper. Yield: 2 dozen.

Glaze:

4 cups sifted powdered sugar
½ teaspoon ground cinnamon
1 teaspoon vanilla extract
¼ cup plus 2 tablespoons milk

Combine all ingredients, and beat until smooth. Yield: about 2 cups.

CHOCOLATE MACAROON MUFFINS

2 cups all-purpose flour
½ cup sugar
3 tablespoons cocoa
1 tablespoon baking powder
¼ teaspoon salt
1 egg, beaten
1 cup milk
⅓ cup vegetable oil
Macaroon Filling

Combine first 5 ingredients in a large bowl; make a well in center of mixture. Combine egg, milk, and oil; add to dry ingredients, stirring just until moistened. Spoon batter into greased muffin pans, filling one-third full. Spoon 2 teaspoons Macaroon Filling in center of each muffin cup; spoon remaining batter over top, filling each muffin cup two-thirds full. Bake at 400° for 20 minutes. Serve warm. Yield: 1 dozen.

Macaroon Filling:

1 cup flaked coconut
¼ cup sweetened condensed milk
¼ teaspoon almond extract

Combine all ingredients, mixing well. Yield: ½ cup.

CHOCOLATE APPLESAUCE BREAD

1½ cups all-purpose flour
1¼ cups sugar
1 teaspoon baking soda
¼ teaspoon baking powder
¼ teaspoon salt
½ teaspoon ground cinnamon
¼ teaspoon ground nutmeg
⅓ cup butter or margarine
2 (1-ounce) squares unsweetened chocolate
½ cup unsweetened applesauce
2 eggs, beaten
½ cup chopped walnuts

Combine first 7 ingredients in a large bowl, mixing well; set aside.

Melt butter and chocolate in a heavy saucepan over low heat. Add chocolate mixture, applesauce, eggs, and walnuts to flour mixture; mix well.

Pour batter into a greased and floured 9- x 5- x 3-inch loafpan. Bake at 350° for 50 to 55 minutes or until a wooden pick inserted in center comes out clean. Cool bread in pan 10 minutes; remove from pan, and cool completely on a wire rack. Yield: 1 loaf.

CHOCOLATE DATE-NUT BREAD

2 (1-ounce) squares unsweetened chocolate
1 cup hot water
1 cup chopped dates
½ cup chopped pecans or walnuts
1 teaspoon baking soda
¼ cup shortening
1 cup sugar
1 egg
2 cups all-purpose flour
½ teaspoon salt
1 teaspoon vanilla extract

Combine chocolate and water in top of a double boiler; bring water to a boil. Reduce heat to low; cook until chocolate melts. Stir in dates, pecans, and soda; cool.

Cream shortening; gradually add sugar, beating well. Add egg, and beat well.

Combine flour and salt; add to creamed mixture alternately with chocolate mixture, beginning and ending with flour mixture. Stir in vanilla.

Pour batter into 2 greased and floured 28-ounce fruit cans. Bake at 350° for 1 hour or until a wooden pick inserted in center comes out clean. Cool in cans 10 minutes; remove from cans, and cool completely. Yield: 2 loaves.

CHOCOLATE CHIP BANANA LOAF

1¾ cups all-purpose flour
¾ teaspoon baking soda
1¼ teaspoons cream of tartar
½ cup chopped walnuts
½ cup semisweet chocolate morsels
¾ cup sugar
½ cup vegetable oil
2 eggs
2 ripe bananas, sliced
½ teaspoon vanilla extract
¼ teaspoon ground cinnamon

Combine flour, soda, cream of tartar, walnuts and chocolate morsels in a large bowl; mix well, and set aside.

Combine remaining ingredients in container of an electric blender; process at medium speed 20 seconds. Stir into flour mixture, mixing well.

Pour batter into a greased 9- x 5- x 3-inch loafpan. Bake at 350° for 50 minutes or until a wooden pick inserted in center comes out clean. Cool in pan 10 minutes; remove from pan, and cool on a wire rack. Yield: 1 loaf.

CHOCOLATE-CINNAMON BUNS

1 package dry yeast
¾ cup warm water (105° to 115°)
¼ cup shortening
½ teaspoon salt
¼ cup sugar
1 egg
⅓ cup cocoa
2¼ cups all-purpose flour, divided
1 tablespoon butter or margarine, softened
3 tablespoons sugar
1½ teaspoons ground cinnamon
¾ cup sifted powdered sugar
1 tablespoon plus 1½ teaspoons milk
¼ cup chopped pecans

Dissolve yeast in warm water. Add shortening, salt, ¼ cup sugar, egg, cocoa, and 1 cup flour. Beat at medium speed of an electric mixer until smooth. Stir in enough remaining flour to make a stiff dough. Place in a well-greased bowl, turning to grease top. Cover and let rise in a warm place (85°), free from drafts, 1 hour or until doubled in bulk.

Punch dough down. Turn dough out onto a lightly floured surface; roll into a 12- x 8-inch rectangle, and spread with butter. Combine 3 tablespoons sugar and cinnamon; sprinkle mixture over rectangle. Roll up jellyroll fashion, beginning at long side; moisten edges with water to seal. Cut rolls into 1-inch slices; place slices cut side down in a lightly greased 9-inch square baking pan. Cover; let rise in a warm place (85°), free from drafts, 1 hour or until doubled in bulk.

Bake at 375° for 20 to 25 minutes. Combine powdered sugar and milk, mixing well. Drizzle glaze over warm rolls. Sprinkle tops with pecans. Yield: 1 dozen.

CHOCOLATE STICKY BUNS

1 package dry yeast
⅓ cup warm water (105° to 115°)
⅓ cup sugar
1 teaspoon salt
½ cup butter or margarine
¾ cup milk, scalded
About 3½ cups all-purpose flour, divided
1 egg, beaten
½ cup butter
1 cup firmly packed brown sugar
¼ cup light corn syrup
3 tablespoons cocoa
1 cup chopped pecans
1 cup sugar
2 tablespoons cocoa
2 teaspoons ground cinnamon
¼ cup butter or margarine, melted

Dissolve yeast in warm water, set aside. Combine ⅓ cup sugar, salt, ½ cup butter, and scalded milk in a mixing bowl; stir until butter melts. Cool to 105° to 115°. Stir in 1½ cups flour, egg, and yeast mixture. Beat at medium speed of an electric mixer 2½ minutes. Stir in enough remaining flour to make a soft dough.

Place dough in a greased bowl, turning to grease top. Cover and let rise in a warm place (85°), free from drafts, about 1 hour or until doubled in bulk.

Melt ½ cup butter in a small saucepan. Add brown sugar, corn syrup, and 3 tablespoons cocoa; bring to a boil and cook, stirring constantly, 1 minute. Pour sugar mixture evenly into two greased 9-inch cakepans. Sprinkle pecans over sugar mixture; set aside.

Combine 1 cup sugar, 2 tablespoons cocoa, and cinnamon; set aside.

Punch dough down, and divide in half. Roll each half into a 14- x 9-inch rectangle; brush with melted butter; sprinkle half of cocoa-cinnamon mixture over each dough rectangle. Starting at widest end, roll up each strip in jellyroll fashion; pinch edges together to seal.

Cut each roll into 1-inch slices. Place 9 slices in each cakepan. Cover and let rise in a warm place (85°), free from drafts, about 1 hour or until doubled in bulk.

Bake at 375° for 25 minutes. Invert pans on serving plates; serve warm. Yield: 1½ dozen.

COCOA-NUT SWIRL BREAD

About 6½ cups all-purpose flour
2 packages dry yeast
1 cup sugar, divided
2 cups milk
½ cup shortening
1½ teaspoons salt
2 eggs
2 tablespoons cocoa
2 tablespoons milk
1 (2½-ounce) package slivered almonds, chopped
Butter or margarine
Glaze (recipe follows)

Combine 3½ cups flour and yeast in a large mixing bowl; stir well.

Combine ½ cup sugar, 2 cups milk, shortening, and salt in a small saucepan; heat until very warm (120° to 130°). Gradually add to flour mixture, stirring well. Add eggs; beat at low speed of an electric mixer 1 minute. Increase to high speed, and beat 3 minutes. Stir in enough remaining flour to make a soft dough.

Turn dough out on a lightly floured surface, and knead until smooth and elastic (about 8 to 10 minutes). Place in a well-greased bowl, turning to grease top. Cover and let rise in a warm place (85°), free from drafts, 40 to 50 minutes or until doubled in bulk.

Punch dough down, and divide in half. Turn out on a lightly floured surface. Roll each half into a 15- x 7-inch rectangle; brush each rectangle lightly with water.

Combine remaining ½ cup sugar, cocoa, and 2 tablespoons milk; mix until smooth, adding additional milk if necessary. Spread half the cocoa mixture evenly over each rectangle; sprinkle with almonds, and dot with butter. Roll up jellyroll fashion, beginning at short end. Fold ends under, and place in a greased 9- x 5- x 3-inch loafpan. Cover and let rise in a warm place (85°), free from drafts, 40 to 50 minutes, or until doubled in bulk. Bake at 375° for 30 to 35 minutes or until loaves sound hollow when tapped. Remove loaves from pans, and transfer to wire racks. Drizzle glaze over warm loaves. Yield: 2 loaves.

Glaze:

1 cup sifted powdered sugar
1½ tablespoons milk
¼ teaspoon vanilla extract

Combine all ingredients, mixing well. Yield: about ½ cup.

Cakes

WINNING FUDGE CAKE

3 (1-ounce) squares unsweetened chocolate
½ cup butter or margarine, softened
2¼ cups firmly packed brown sugar
3 eggs
1½ teaspoons vanilla extract
2¼ cups sifted cake flour
2 teaspoons baking soda
½ teaspoon salt
1 (8-ounce) carton commercial sour cream
1 cup boiling water
Filling (recipe follows)
Mocha Frosting
Chocolate curls (optional)
Grated chocolate (optional)

Melt chocolate in a heavy saucepan over low heat; set aside to cool. Cream butter in a large mixing bowl; gradually add sugar, beating well at medium speed of an electric mixer. Add eggs, one at a time, beating well after each addition. Add chocolate and vanilla; mix well.

Combine flour, soda, and salt; add to creamed mixture alternately with sour cream, beginning and ending with flour mixture. Stir in boiling water. (Batter will be thin.)

Pour batter into 2 greased and floured 8-inch round cakepans. Bake at 350° for 30 to 35 minutes or until a wooden pick inserted in center comes out clean. Cool in pans 10 minutes; remove from pans, and cool completely on wire racks. Split cake layers in half horizontally to make 4 layers. Spread filling between layers; spread Mocha Frosting on top and sides of cake. Refrigerate. Garnish with chocolate curls and grated chocolate, if desired. Yield: one 4-layer cake.

Filling:

1½ cups whipping cream
1 teaspoon vanilla extract
½ cup sifted powdered sugar

Beat whipping cream and vanilla until foamy; gradually add powdered sugar, beating until soft peaks form. Yield: enough for one 4-layer cake.

Mocha Frosting:

½ cup butter or margarine, softened
5 cups sifted powdered sugar
¼ cup cocoa
¼ cup strong coffee
2 teaspoons vanilla extract
About 2 tablespoons whipping cream

Cream butter; gradually add sugar, cocoa, coffee, and vanilla, beating at low speed of an electric mixer until light and fluffy. Add cream if too stiff, and beat well. Yield: enough for one 4-layer cake.

FAVORITE CHOCOLATE CAKE

½ cup shortening
2 cups sugar
2 eggs
4 (1-ounce) squares unsweetened chocolate, melted
2 cups sifted cake flour
½ teaspoon baking powder
1 teaspoon baking soda
1 teaspoon salt
¾ cup buttermilk
¾ cup water
1 teaspoon vanilla extract
Chocolate filling (recipe follows)
Chocolate frosting (recipe follows)

Cream shortening; gradually add sugar, beating well at medium speed of an electric mixer. Add eggs, one at a time, beating well after each addition. Add chocolate, mixing well.

Combine flour, baking powder, soda, and salt; gradually add to the chocolate mixture alternately with buttermilk, beating well after each addition. Add water, mixing well; stir in vanilla.

Line bottom of two greased 9-inch round cakepans with wax paper. Pour batter evenly into pans; bake at 350° for 30 minutes or until a wooden pick inserted in center comes out clean.

Cool in pans 10 minutes; remove from pans and cool completely on wire racks. Peel off wax paper.

Spread chocolate filling between layers. Frost top and sides of cake with chocolate frosting. Yield: one 2-layer cake.

Chocolate Filling:

2 tablespoons cornstarch
½ cup sugar
Dash of salt
½ cup water
1 tablespoon butter or margarine
2 (1-ounce) squares semisweet chocolate

Combine cornstarch, sugar, salt, and water in small saucepan; cook over medium heat, stirring constantly, until thickened and bubbly. Remove from heat. Add butter and chocolate; stir until melted and smooth. Cool. Yield: enough for one 2-layer cake.

Chocolate Frosting:

2 cups sugar
1 cup evaporated milk
½ cup butter or margarine
1 (6-ounce) package semisweet chocolate morsels
1 cup marshmallow creme
3 to 4 tablespoons milk

Combine first 3 ingredients in a medium saucepan; cook over medium heat, stirring constantly, until mixture reaches soft ball stage (238°). Remove from heat; add chocolate, marshmallow creme, and 3 tablespoons milk, stirring until smooth. Cool slightly; beat at medium speed of an electric mixer until thick enough to spread, adding additional milk if necessary. Yield: enough for one 2-layer cake.

VELVETY CHOCOLATE CAKE

½ cup buttermilk
1 teaspoon baking soda
2 cups all-purpose flour
2 cups sugar
¼ teaspoon salt
½ cup butter or margarine
1 cup water
¼ cup cocoa
2 eggs, beaten
Velvety Chocolate Frosting

Combine buttermilk and soda. Combine flour, sugar, and salt. Combine butter, water, and cocoa in a saucepan; bring to a boil. Pour over flour mixture; cool. Add eggs and buttermilk mixture; mix well.

Pour into 2 greased and floured 8-inch round cakepans. Bake at 350° for 25 to 30 minutes or until a wooden pick inserted in center comes out clean. Cool 10 minutes; remove from pans and cool on wire racks. Spread with warm Velvety Chocolate Frosting. Yield: one 2-layer cake.

Velvety Chocolate Frosting:

½ cup butter or margarine
¼ cup plus 2 tablespoons milk
¼ cup cocoa
1 (16-ounce) package powdered sugar

Combine butter, milk, and cocoa in a saucepan; bring to a boil. Remove from heat; add powdered sugar, stirring well. Yield: enough for one 2-layer cake.

SOUR CREAM CHOCOLATE CAKE

4 (1-ounce) squares unsweetened chocolate
1 cup hot water
2 eggs, beaten
2 cups sugar
1 (8-ounce) carton commercial sour cream
2 teaspoons vanilla extract
2 cups all-purpose flour
1 teaspoon baking soda
½ teaspoon salt
Frosting (recipe follows)

Combine chocolate and hot water in a small saucepan; place over low heat, stirring until chocolate melts. Remove from heat, and set aside.

Combine eggs and sugar in a medium mixing bowl, mixing well; add sour cream, chocolate mixture, and vanilla. Mix well.

Combine flour, soda, and salt; gradually add to chocolate mixture, mixing well. Pour into 2 greased and floured 8-inch round cakepans. Bake at 300° for 55 minutes or until a wooden pick inserted in center comes out clean. Cool before removing from pans. Spread frosting between layers and on top and sides of cake. Yield: one 2-layer cake.

Frosting:

2 cups sugar
¼ cup cocoa
½ cup butter or margarine
1 tablespoon light corn syrup
½ cup milk
1 cup chopped pecans
1 teaspoon vanilla extract

Combine sugar and cocoa in a small saucepan, mixing well. Add margarine, corn syrup, and milk; bring to a boil, and boil 2 minutes. Remove from heat, and cool 5 minutes. Beat at medium speed of an electric mixer until thick enough to spread. Stir in pecans and vanilla. Yield: enough for one 2-layer cake.

CHOCOLATE RUM CAKE

2 (1-ounce) squares unsweetened chocolate
½ cup water
½ cup butter, softened
1½ cups firmly packed light brown sugar
3 eggs
1¾ cups sifted cake flour
1½ teaspoons baking powder
½ teaspoon baking soda
¼ teaspoon salt
¼ cup rum
Chocolate Rum Frosting

Grease two 9-inch cakepans; line with wax paper, and grease again. Set aside.

Combine chocolate and water in a small saucepan; place over low heat, stirring until chocolate melts. Set aside to cool.

Cream butter; gradually add sugar, beating well at medium speed of an electric mixer. Add eggs, one at a time, beating well after each addition.

Combine flour, baking powder, soda, and salt; add to creamed mixture alternately with chocolate, mixing well after each addition. Stir in rum.

Spoon batter into cakepans; bake at 350° for 20 to 25 minutes or until a wooden pick inserted in center comes out clean. Cool 5 minutes in pans; remove from pans, peel off wax paper, and cool on wire racks. Spread frosting between layers and on top of cake only. Yield: one 2-layer cake.

Chocolate Rum Frosting:

3 tablespoons semisweet chocolate morsels
1½ (1-ounce) squares unsweetened chocolate
1 tablespoon butter or margarine
1 cup sifted powdered sugar
¼ cup egg substitute
2 tablespoons milk
2 tablespoons rum
Powdered sugar

Combine chocolate and butter in top of a double boiler; bring water to a boil. Reduce heat to low; cook until chocolate melts.

Combine 1 cup powdered sugar, egg substitute, milk, and rum; mix until smooth. Stir in chocolate mixture. Place bowl in a larger bowl of ice water; beat until thickened, adding additional powdered sugar, if needed for good spreading consistency. Yield: enough for two 9-inch layers.

BROWN SUGAR FUDGE CAKE

½ cup shortening
2 cups firmly packed brown sugar
3 eggs
2 (1-ounce) squares unsweetened chocolate, melted
2¼ cups sifted cake flour
1 teaspoon baking soda
½ teaspoon salt
1 cup buttermilk
1 teaspoon vanilla extract
Creamy Chocolate Frosting
Chocolate curls
Grated semisweet chocolate

Cream shortening; gradually add sugar, beating at medium speed of an electric mixer. Add eggs, beating well after each addition. Add chocolate; beat well.

Combine flour, soda, and salt; add to creamed mixture alternately with buttermilk. Mix just until blended after each addition. Stir in vanilla.

Pour batter into 3 greased and floured 8-inch round cakepans. Bake at 350° for 25 to 30 minutes or until a wooden pick inserted in center comes out clean. Cool in pans 10 minutes; remove from pans, and cool completely on wire racks. Spread Creamy Chocolate Frosting between layers and on top and sides of cake. Garnish with chocolate curls and grated chocolate. Yield: one 3-layer cake.

Creamy Chocolate Frosting:

¾ cup butter or margarine
¾ cup cocoa
½ cup milk
¼ teaspoon salt
2¼ teaspoons vanilla extract
6¾ cups sifted powdered sugar

Combine butter, cocoa, and milk in a small saucepan; cook over low heat, stirring constantly, until butter melts. Remove from heat; add salt and vanilla. Gradually add powdered sugar, 1 cup at a time, beating at high speed of an electric mixer until thick enough to spread, adding additional milk, if necessary. Yield: enough for one 3-layer cake.

CHOCOLATE-PEANUT BUTTER CAKE

3¼ cups all-purpose flour
2¼ cups sugar
1 tablespoon plus 1 teaspoon baking powder
½ teaspoon salt
½ cup butter or margarine, softened
½ cup creamy peanut butter
1½ cups milk
3 eggs
1⅓ cups finely chopped unsalted roasted peanuts
Chocolate-Peanut Butter Frosting
1 (6-ounce) package semisweet chocolate morsels
2 to 4 tablespoons chopped unsalted roasted peanuts

Combine first 4 ingredients in a large mixing bowl; mix well. Add butter, peanut butter, and milk; beat 2 minutes at medium speed of an electric mixer. Add eggs; beat 2 minutes at medium speed. Fold in 1⅓ cups chopped peanuts.

Pour batter into 3 greased and floured 9-inch round cakepans. Bake at 350° for 25 to 30 minutes or until a wooden pick inserted in center comes out clean (do not overbake). Cool in pans 10 minutes; remove layers from pans, and cool completely on wire racks.

Spread Chocolate-Peanut Butter Frosting between layers and on top and sides of cake; chill 1 hour or until firm.

Melt chocolate morsels in top of a double boiler over hot water. Drizzle around top edge and down sides of cake. Sprinkle 2 to 4 tablespoons chopped peanuts on top. Chill until ready to serve. Yield: one 3-layer cake.

Chocolate-Peanut Butter Frosting:

1 (6-ounce) package semisweet chocolate morsels
½ cup butter or margarine, softened
½ cup sifted powdered sugar
1⅓ cups creamy peanut butter

Melt chocolate morsels in top of a double boiler over hot water, and set aside. Combine remaining ingredients in a small mixing bowl; beat at medium speed of an electric mixer until smooth. Add melted chocolate to peanut butter mixture; beat until smooth. Chill 15 minutes or until thick enough to spread. Yield: enough for one 3-layer cake.

CHOCOLATE CARAMEL CAKE

3 (1-ounce) squares unsweetened chocolate
⅔ cup butter or margarine, softened
1½ cups sugar
½ cup firmly packed brown sugar
3 eggs
2⅓ cups sifted cake flour
2 teaspoons baking soda
½ teaspoon salt
1⅓ cups buttermilk
⅓ cup water
1¼ teaspoons vanilla extract
Caramel Filling
½ cup chopped pecans, divided
Fluffy Marshmallow Frosting
2 (1-ounce) squares unsweetened chocolate (optional)
Grated chocolate (optional)

Melt 3 squares chocolate in a heavy saucepan over low heat, stirring constantly; cool slightly.

Cream butter; gradually add sugar, beating at medium speed of an electric mixer until light and fluffy. Add chocolate; mix well. Add eggs, one at a time, beating well after each addition.

Combine flour, soda, and salt; add to creamed mixture alternately with buttermilk, beginning and ending with flour mixture. Mix well after each addition. Stir in water and vanilla.

Pour batter into 3 greased and floured 9-inch round cakepans. Bake at 350° for 25 to 30 minutes or until a wooden pick inserted in center comes out clean. Cool in pans 10 minutes; remove layers from pans, and cool completely on wire racks.

Spread half of Caramel Filling on top of one layer; sprinkle with ¼ cup pecans.

Carefully spread a ½-inch-thick layer of Fluffy Marshmallow Frosting over pecans; place second cake layer on top. Repeat filling, pecan, and frosting layers; top with remaining cake layer. Spread remaining frosting over top and sides of cake.

Melt 2 squares chocolate, if desired, in a heavy saucepan over low heat, stirring constantly; cool slightly. Drizzle melted chocolate around edges and down sides of cake. Sprinkle grated chocolate over center of cake, if desired. Yield: one 3-layer cake.

Caramel Filling:

1 cup firmly packed brown sugar
3 tablespoons all-purpose flour
1 cup evaporated milk
2 egg yolks, slightly beaten
2 tablespoons butter or margarine, softened

Combine sugar and flour in a saucepan; gradually stir in milk. Cook over medium heat, stirring constantly, until mixture thickens and boils. Boil 1 minute, stirring constantly; remove from heat. Gradually stir about one-fourth of hot mixture into yolks; add to remaining hot mixture, stirring constantly. Return to a boil and boil 1 minute, stirring constantly. Remove from heat; add butter, stirring until butter melts. Let cool. Yield: enough for two 9-inch layers.

Fluffy Marshmallow Frosting:

2 egg whites
1½ cups sugar
1 tablespoon plus 2 teaspoons light corn syrup
⅓ cup water
16 large marshmallows, quartered

Combine egg whites, sugar, corn syrup, and water in top of a double boiler; beat 1 minute at high speed of an electric mixer. Place over boiling water and beat at high speed 7 minutes or until temperature reaches 160°. Remove from heat; transfer to a large mixing bowl. Add marshmallows; beat until good spreading consistency. Yield: enough for one 3-layer cake.

BROWN MOUNTAIN CAKE

1 cup butter or margarine, softened
2 cups sugar
3 eggs
3 cups all-purpose flour
1 cup buttermilk
½ cup warm water
3 tablespoons cocoa
1 teaspoon baking soda
1 teaspoon vanilla extract
Caramel frosting (recipe follows)
Grated chocolate (optional)
Pecan halves (optional)

Cream butter; gradually add sugar, beating at medium speed of an electric mixer until light and fluffy. Add eggs, one at a time, beating well after each addition. Add flour alternately with buttermilk, beginning and ending with flour. Combine water, cocoa, and soda, stirring well; slowly add to flour mixture, beating well. Stir in vanilla.

Pour batter into 2 greased and floured 9-inch round cakepans. Bake at 350° for 35 to 40 minutes or until a wooden pick inserted in center comes out clean. Cool in pans 10 minutes; remove from pans, and cool completely on wire racks.

Spread caramel frosting between layers and on top and sides of cake. Sprinkle with grated chocolate, and garnish with pecan halves, if desired. Yield: one 2-layer cake.

Caramel Frosting:

1 cup butter
2 cups sugar
1 cup evaporated milk
1 teaspoon vanilla extract

Melt butter in a heavy saucepan over medium heat; add sugar and milk. Cook mixture over medium heat, stirring constantly, until mixture reaches soft ball stage (234°). Remove from heat, and add vanilla (do not stir); cool 10 minutes.

Beat frosting at medium speed of an electric mixer about 10 minutes or until thick enough to spread. Spread immediately on cooled cake. Yield: enough for one 2-layer cake.

WHITE CHOCOLATE CAKE

¼ pound white chocolate, coarsely chopped
½ cup boiling water
1 cup butter or margarine, softened
2 cups sugar
4 eggs, separated
1 teaspoon vanilla extract
2½ cups sifted cake flour
1 teaspoon baking soda
1 cup buttermilk
Coconut-Pecan Frosting

Combine chocolate and water, stirring until chocolate melts; set aside.

Cream butter; gradually add sugar, beating well at medium speed of an electric mixer. Add egg yolks, one at a time, beating well after each addition. Stir in chocolate mixture and vanilla.

Combine flour and soda; add to chocolate mixture alternately with buttermilk, beginning and ending with flour mixture. Beat egg whites (at room temperature) until stiff peaks form; fold into chocolate mixture.

Pour batter into 3 well-greased and floured 9-inch round cakepans. Bake at 350° for 25 minutes or until a wooden pick inserted in center comes out clean. Cool in pans 10 minutes; remove and cool completely on wire racks. Spread Coconut-Pecan Frosting between layers and on top and sides of cake. Yield: one 3-layer cake.

Coconut-Pecan Frosting:

1 cup evaporated milk
1½ cups sugar
¼ cup plus 2 tablespoons butter or margarine
4 egg yolks
1½ cups flaked coconut
1½ cups chopped pecans
1½ teaspoons vanilla extract

Combine first 4 ingredients in a heavy saucepan; bring to a boil and cook over medium heat 12 minutes, stirring constantly. Add coconut, pecans, and vanilla; stir until cool and thick enough to spread. Yield: enough for one 3-layer cake.

DARK MOCHA-CHOCOLATE CAKE

1 tablespoon butter or margarine
2 tablespoons fine, dry breadcrumbs
4 (1-ounce) squares unsweetened chocolate
½ cup water
¼ cup instant coffee granules
½ cup butter or margarine, softened
1 cup sugar
2 eggs
1¾ cups all-purpose flour
2 teaspoons baking powder
1 teaspoon ground cinnamon
¼ teaspoon ground cloves
½ cup milk
1 teaspoon vanilla extract
Cinnamon-Cream Frosting

Grease two 8-inch round cakepans with 1 tablespoon butter; sprinkle breadcrumbs on bottom and sides of pans. Set aside.

Combine chocolate, water, and coffee granules in top of a double boiler; bring water to a boil. Reduce heat to low; cook until chocolate melts.

Cream ½ cup butter; gradually add sugar, beating well at medium speed of an electric mixer. Add eggs, one at a time, beating well after each addition. Add chocolate mixture, and beat well.

Combine flour and next 3 ingredients. Add to creamed mixture alternately with milk, beating at low speed of an electric mixer, beginning and ending with flour mixture. Do not overbeat.

Pour batter into cakepans. Bake at 350° for 20 to 25 minutes or until a wooden pick inserted in center comes out clean. Cool in pans 10 minutes; remove layers from pans, and cool completely on wire racks. Spread Cinnamon-Cream Frosting between layers and on top of cake only. Yield: one 2-layer cake.

Cinnamon-Cream Frosting:

1 cup whipping cream
2 tablespoons sugar
1 tablespoon coffee granules
¼ teaspoon ground cinnamon

Beat whipping cream until foamy; gradually add sugar, coffee granules, and cinnamon, beating until stiff peaks form. Yield: enough for two 8-inch layers.

VANILLA-FILLED CHOCOLATE CAKE

2 (1-ounce) squares unsweetened chocolate
3 tablespoons water
¾ cup butter or margarine, softened
2¼ cups sugar
4 eggs, separated
1 teaspoon vanilla extract
2¼ cups sifted cake flour
1 teaspoon cream of tartar
½ teaspoon baking soda
½ teaspoon salt
1 cup milk
Vanilla Cream Filling
Chocolate-Cream Cheese Frosting
¼ cup chopped almonds, toasted

Combine chocolate and water in a small saucepan; cook over low heat, stirring constantly, until chocolate melts. Cool slightly.

Cream butter; gradually add sugar, beating well at medium speed of an electric mixer. Add egg yolks, one at a time, beating well after each addition. Add chocolate mixture and vanilla; mix well.

Combine flour, cream of tartar, soda, and salt; add to creamed mixture alternately with milk, beginning and ending with flour mixture. Mix well after each addition. Beat egg whites (at room temperature) at high speed of an electric mixer until stiff peaks form; fold into batter.

Pour batter into 3 greased and floured 9-inch round cakepans; bake at 350° for 25 to 30 minutes or until a wooden pick inserted in center comes out clean. Cool in pans 10 minutes; remove from pans, and cool completely on wire racks.

Spread Vanilla Cream Filling between layers. Spread Chocolate-Cream Cheese Frosting on top and sides of cake. Sprinkle almonds over top of cake, if desired. Chill cake 3 to 4 hours before serving. Yield: one 3-layer cake.

Vanilla Cream Filling:

½ cup sugar
3 tablespoons all-purpose flour
⅛ teaspoon salt
1½ cups milk
2 eggs, beaten
¼ cup chopped almonds, toasted
½ teaspoon vanilla extract

Combine sugar, flour, and salt in a heavy saucepan; gradually stir in milk. Cook over medium heat, stirring constantly, until smooth and thickened. Gradually stir about one-fourth of hot mixture into eggs; add to remaining hot mixture, stirring constantly. Bring to a boil; cook, stirring constantly, 2 to 3 minutes or until thickened. Remove from heat; stir in almonds and vanilla. Cover and chill 1 to 2 hours. Yield: enough for one 3-layer cake.

Chocolate-Cream Cheese Frosting:

3 (1-ounce) squares unsweetened chocolate
¼ cup butter or margarine, softened
1 (8-ounce) package cream cheese, softened
3 cups sifted powdered sugar, divided
1 tablespoon plus 1 teaspoon whipping cream
Dash of salt
½ teaspoon vanilla extract

Melt chocolate in a heavy saucepan over low heat, stirring constantly; cool.

Cream butter and cream cheese; add 1 cup powdered sugar, chocolate, whipping cream, salt, and vanilla, beating well at low speed of an electric mixer. Add remaining sugar; beat until thick enough to spread. Yield: enough for one 3-layer cake.

DOUBLE MOCHA CAKE

1 cup shortening
2½ cups sugar
5 eggs, separated
3 cups all-purpose flour
¼ cup cocoa
1 teaspoon baking soda
½ teaspoon salt
1 cup buttermilk
¼ cup plus 1 tablespoon brewed cold coffee
2 teaspoons vanilla extract
Creamy Mocha Frosting
Chocolate leaves or chocolate curls (optional)

Cream shortening; gradually add sugar, beating well at medium speed of an electric mixer. Beat egg yolks; add to creamed mixture, and beat well. Combine flour, cocoa, soda, and salt; add to creamed mixture alternately with buttermilk, beginning and ending with flour mixture. Stir in coffee and vanilla.

Beat egg whites (at room temperature) until stiff peaks form; fold into batter.

Pour batter into 3 greased and floured 9-inch round cakepans. Bake at 350° for 20 to 25 minutes or until a wooden pick inserted in center comes out clean. Cool in pans 10 minutes; remove layers from pans, and cool completely on wire racks. Spread Creamy Mocha Frosting between layers and on top and sides of cake. Garnish with chocolate leaves, if desired. Yield: one 3-layer cake.

Creamy Mocha Frosting:

¾ cup butter or margarine, softened
5½ to 6 cups sifted powdered sugar
1 tablespoon cocoa
¼ cup plus 1½ teaspoons brewed cold coffee
1½ teaspoons vanilla extract

Cream butter. Combine 5½ cups sugar and cocoa; gradually add to butter, beating at low speed of an electric mixer until smooth. Add remaining ingredients; beat until fluffy, adding enough remaining sugar to make good spreading consistency. Yield: enough for one 3-layer cake.

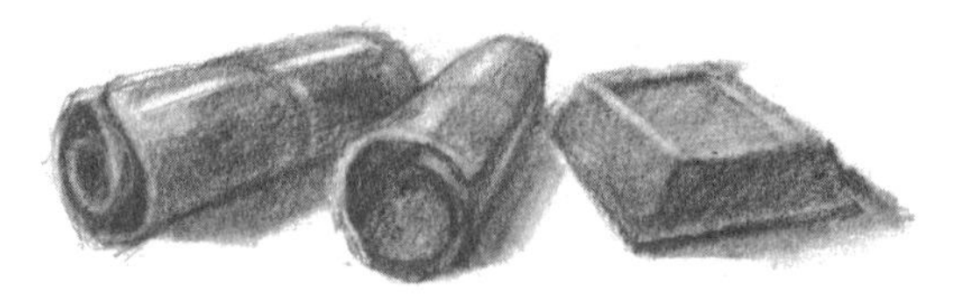

BELGIAN MOCHA CAKE

½ cup sugar
3 tablespoons water
2 (1-ounce) squares unsweetened chocolate
¾ cup butter or margarine, softened
2 cups sugar
1 teaspoon vanilla extract
4 eggs, separated
2¼ cups cake flour
½ teaspoon baking soda
½ teaspoon salt
1 cup milk
1 teaspoon cream of tartar
Mocha frosting (recipe follows)
Chocolate curls or grated chocolate (optional)

Combine ½ cup sugar, water, and chocolate in a heavy saucepan; cook over low heat, stirring until chocolate melts. Remove from heat; cool.

Cream butter; gradually add sugar, beating well at medium speed of an electric mixer. Stir in vanilla. Add egg yolks, one at a time, beating well after each addition. Stir in chocolate mixture.

Combine flour, soda, and salt; add to creamed mixture alternately with milk, beginning and ending with flour mixture. Mix well after each addition. Beat egg whites (at room temperature) at high speed of an electric mixer until frothy; add cream of tartar, and beat until stiff peaks form. Fold into batter.

Grease three 9-inch round cakepans; line with wax paper; grease again and dust with flour. Pour batter into pans; bake at 350° for 25 to 30 minutes or until a wooden pick inserted in center comes out clean. Remove layers; cool on wire racks.

Spread mocha frosting between layers and on top and sides of cake. Store in refrigerator. Garnish with chocolate curls, if desired. Yield: one 3-layer cake.

Mocha Frosting:

1 cup butter, softened
2 to 2¼ cups sifted powdered sugar, divided
1 tablespoon instant coffee granules
¾ teaspoon cocoa
¾ teaspoon hot water
2½ tablespoons egg substitute
1 to 1½ tablespoons almond extract
2 tablespoons rum

Cream butter and 1½ cups powdered sugar, beating at low speed of an electric mixer until light and fluffy. Combine coffee granules, cocoa, and water; stir into creamed mixture. Add egg substitute, and beat 5 minutes. Stir in almond extract and rum. Add enough of remaining sugar to make thick enough to spread (frosting gets quite firm when refrigerated). Yield: enough for one 3-layer cake.

CHOCOLATE VELVET TORTE

8 (1-ounce) squares sweet baking chocolate
¾ cup butter or margarine
¼ cup plus 2 tablespoons all-purpose flour
6 eggs, separated
½ cup sugar
⅔ cup raspberry preserves
Chocolate glaze (recipe follows)

Combine chocolate and butter in a heavy saucepan; cook over low heat until melted, stirring often. Remove from heat, and stir in flour. Add egg yolks, one at a time, stirring well after each addition; set aside.

Beat egg whites (at room temperature) at high speed of an electric mixer until foamy; gradually add sugar, 1 tablespoon at a time, beating until stiff peaks form and sugar dissolves.

Fold egg whites into chocolate mixture. Pour into 3 greased and floured 8-inch round cakepans; bake at 350° for 20 to 25 minutes or until a wooden pick inserted in center comes out clean. Cool in pans 10 minutes (layers settle as they cool). Remove layers; cool on wire racks.

Spread ⅓ cup raspberry preserves between each layer; drizzle chocolate glaze on top. Yield: one 3-layer torte.

Chocolate Glaze:

4 (1-ounce) squares sweet baking chocolate
2 tablespoons water
3 tablespoons butter or margarine, softened

Combine chocolate and water in a heavy saucepan; cook over low heat until melted, stirring often. Remove from heat; stir in butter. Cool until desired consistency, stirring occasionally. Yield: enough for one 3-layer torte.

MOCHA BROWNIE TORTE

1 (15.5-ounce) package fudge brownie mix
2 eggs, beaten
2 tablespoons water
½ cup chopped pecans
1 cup whipping cream
3 tablespoons plus 1 teaspoon brown sugar
2 teaspoons instant coffee granules
Additional flavored whipped cream for piping (optional)
Shaved chocolate (optional)
Chocolate curls (optional)

Lightly grease two 8-inch round cakepans; line with wax paper, and grease again. Set aside.

Combine brownie mix, eggs, and water; mix well. Stir in pecans. Spread batter in pans. Bake at 350° for 15 to 18 minutes. Cool 5 minutes; remove layers from pans, and cool completely on wire racks.

Beat whipping cream until foamy; gradually add sugar and coffee granules, beating until stiff peaks form.

Spread whipped cream mixture between layers and on top and sides of cake. Garnish with piped whipped cream mixture, shaved chocolate, and chocolate curls, if desired. Chill until serving time. Yield: one 2-layer torte.

CHOCOLATE CHIP-SOUR CREAM CAKE

½ cup butter or margarine, softened
1 cup sugar
2 eggs
2 cups all-purpose flour
1 teaspoon baking powder
1 teaspoon baking soda
1 (8-ounce) carton sour cream
1 teaspoon vanilla extract
1 (6-ounce) package semisweet chocolate morsels
1 cup chopped pecans
¼ cup firmly packed brown sugar

Cream butter; gradually add 1 cup sugar, beating at medium speed until light and fluffy. Add eggs, beating well.

Combine flour, baking powder, and soda; stir one-third of dry ingredients into creamed mixture. Stir in half of sour cream. Repeat procedure, ending with flour mixture. Stir in vanilla.

Combine chocolate, pecans, and brown sugar; set aside. Spoon half of batter into a greased and floured 10-inch tube pan. Sprinkle with half of chocolate mixture. Spoon in remaining batter; top with remaining chocolate mixture. Bake at 350° for 50 minutes or until a wooden pick comes out clean. Remove from pan; cool completely. Yield: one 10-inch cake.

CHOCOLATE SPONGE CAKE

2 cups superfine sugar
¾ cup all-purpose flour
½ cup cocoa
12 eggs, divided
1 teaspoon cream of tartar
1 teaspoon vanilla extract

Sift sugar, flour, and cocoa together.

Beat egg whites at high speed of an electric mixer until foamy. Add cream of tartar and vanilla; beat until soft peaks form.

Sprinkle one-fourth of flour mixture over whites; gently fold in with a spatula. Repeat with remaining flour mixture, adding one-fourth at a time. Spoon into an ungreased 10-inch tube pan with removable bottom. Bake at 375° for 40 minutes or until cake springs back when touched lightly. Invert pan on funnel for 2 hours or until cooled. Loosen cake from sides of pan; gently remove cake from pan. Yield: one 10-inch cake.

ROCKY ROAD CAKE

2¼ cups sugar, divided
1 cup vegetable oil
3 large eggs
3 cups all-purpose flour
¾ cup cocoa
2 teaspoons baking soda
2 teaspoons baking powder
1½ teaspoons salt
1 cup brewed coffee or water
1 cup buttermilk
½ cup chopped pecans
4 teaspoons vanilla extract, divided
1 (8-ounce) package cream cheese, softened
½ cup flaked coconut
1 cup semisweet chocolate morsels
2 tablespoons butter or margarine
1 cup powdered sugar
3 tablespoons cocoa
1 to 3 tablespoons hot water

Beat 2 cups sugar, oil, and 2 eggs at high speed of electric mixer 1 minute.

Combine flour and next 4 ingredients; combine coffee and buttermilk. Add both mixtures to oil mixture. Beat at medium speed 3 minutes. Stir in nuts and 1 teaspoon vanilla. Pour half of batter into a greased, floured 12-cup Bundt pan.

Beat cream cheese until fluffy; gradually add remaining sugar and egg. Beat until blended. Stir in 1 teaspoon vanilla, coconut, and morsels; spoon over batter, leaving ½-inch border around center and edge. Top with remaining batter.

Bake at 350° for 1 hour and 10 minutes or until a wooden pick comes out clean. Cool in pan on a wire rack 15 minutes. Remove from pan; cool completely.

Melt butter; stir in remaining 2 teaspoons vanilla, powdered sugar, cocoa, and hot water. Drizzle over cooled cake. Yield: 1 (10-inch) cake.

HOLIDAY LOG CAKE

¾ teaspoon baking powder
¼ teaspoon salt
4 eggs
¾ cup sugar
¾ cup all-purpose flour
¼ cup cocoa
1 teaspoon vanilla extract
2 to 3 tablespoons powdered sugar
2 cups sweetened whipped cream
3 (1-ounce) squares unsweetened chocolate
¼ cup butter or margarine
1 tablespoon instant coffee granules
Dash of salt
⅓ cup boiling water
About 2½ cups powdered sugar
Candied cherries

Lightly grease a 15- x 10- x 1-inch jellyroll pan; line with wax paper, and grease lightly. Set aside.

Combine baking powder, ¼ teaspoon salt, and eggs (at room temperature) in mixing bowl; beat at medium speed of an electric mixer until blended. Gradually add sugar, beating until thick and lemon colored. Fold in flour, cocoa, and vanilla.

Spread mixture evenly into prepared pan. Bake at 400° for 13 minutes or until surface springs back when gently pressed.

Sift 2 to 3 tablespoons powdered sugar in a 15- x 10-inch rectangle on a linen towel. Turn cake out on sugar; remove wax paper from cake. Trim edges, if necessary. Starting with short end, roll up cake and towel, jellyroll fashion. Cool thoroughly on wire rack. Unroll; spread with whipped cream, and reroll. Chill.

Place chocolate in top of a double boiler; bring water to a boil. Reduce heat to low; cook until chocolate melts. Blend in butter, coffee, dash of salt, and boiling water, stirring until smooth. Cool to lukewarm. Stir in about 2½ cups powdered sugar to make a spreading consistency.

Spread frosting evenly over cake. Mark frosting with tines of a fork to resemble bark of a tree and decorate with candied cherries. Refrigerate until serving time. Yield 8 to 10 servings.

ROLLED CHOCOLATE ICE CREAM CAKE

½ cup all-purpose flour
⅓ cup cocoa
1 teaspoon baking powder
¼ teaspoon salt
4 eggs, separated
¾ cup sugar
½ teaspoon vanilla extract
¼ teaspoon almond extract
1 quart vanilla ice cream, softened
Chocolate frosting (recipe follows)
Chopped dry-roasted pistachios
Whole dry-roasted pistachios

Grease a 15- x 10- x 1-inch jellyroll pan. Line with wax paper; grease again. Sift first 4 ingredients together; set aside.

Beat egg whites (at room temperature) at high speed of an electric mixer until foamy. Gradually add sugar, beating until soft peaks form; set aside.

Beat egg yolks until thick and lemon colored; stir in flavorings. Fold yolk mixture into egg white mixture; then gently fold in flour mixture. Spread evenly in prepared pan. Bake at 350° for 12 minutes.

When cake is done, immediately loosen from sides of pan and turn out onto a damp towel. Peel off wax paper. Starting at wide end, roll up cake and towel together; cool 30 minutes on wire rack, seam side down.

Unroll cake; remove towel. Spread ice cream over cake. Gently roll cake back up; place on a large baking sheet, seam side down. Freeze until ice cream is firm.

Frost cake with chocolate frosting; freeze until serving time. Sprinkle with pistachios. Yield: 8 to 10 servings.

Chocolate Frosting:

¼ cup butter or margarine, softened
3 tablespoons milk
3 tablespoons cocoa
2 cups sifted powdered sugar
1 teaspoon vanilla extract

Combine all ingredients; beat until smooth. Yield: enough frosting for one cake roll.

CHOCOLATE CHIP COFFEE CAKE

1 cup butter or margarine, softened
1 cup sugar
3 eggs
3 cups all-purpose flour
1 tablespoon baking powder
1 teaspoon baking soda
½ teaspoon salt
1 (8-ounce) carton commercial sour cream
1 (12-ounce) package semisweet chocolate morsels
½ cup firmly packed brown sugar
1 teaspoon ground cinnamon

Cream butter; gradually add sugar, beating at medium speed of an electric mixer until light and fluffy. Add eggs, one at a time, beating well after each addition.

Combine flour, baking powder, soda, and salt; add to creamed mixture alternately with sour cream, beginning and ending with flour mixture. Spoon half of batter into a greased and floured 13- x 9- x 2-inch baking pan.

Combine chocolate morsels, brown sugar, and cinnamon; sprinkle 1½ cups of chocolate morsel mixture over batter. Top with remaining batter. Sprinkle with remaining chocolate morsel mixture. Bake at 350° for 35 to 40 minutes. Serve warm or at room temperature. Yield: 15 to 18 servings.

BUTTERMILK CHOCOLATE CAKE

2 cups all-purpose flour
2 cups sugar
1 teaspoon baking soda
1 cup water
½ cup butter or margarine
¼ cup cocoa
2 eggs
½ cup buttermilk
Coconut Chocolate Frosting

Combine flour, sugar, and soda in a large mixing bowl. Combine water, butter, and cocoa in a small saucepan; cook over low heat until mixture comes to a boil; remove from heat and pour over dry ingredients, mixing thoroughly. Add eggs and buttermilk; beat well.

Spoon batter into a well-greased 13- x 9- x 2-inch baking pan. Bake at 350° for 30 minutes or until a wooden pick inserted in center comes out clean. Cool in pan. Frost with Coconut Chocolate Frosting. Yield: 15 to 18 servings.

Coconut Chocolate Frosting:

1 (16-ounce) package powdered sugar
1 cup chopped pecans
1 cup shredded coconut
⅓ cup plus 2 teaspoons milk
½ cup butter or margarine
3 tablespoons cocoa

Combine powdered sugar, pecans, and coconut in a large mixing bowl; set aside. Combine milk, butter, and cocoa in a small saucepan; cook over low heat, stirring until mixture comes to a boil. Add chocolate mixture to sugar mixture; beat with an electric mixer until frosting is fluffy. Yield: enough for one 13- x 9- x 2-inch cake.

CHOCOLATE CANDY CAKE

2 cups all-purpose flour
2 cups sugar
1 teaspoon baking soda
1 cup water
1 cup butter or margarine
¼ cup cocoa
½ cup buttermilk
2 eggs, slightly beaten
1 teaspoon vanilla extract
Chocolate Candy Frosting

Combine flour, sugar, and soda; mix well, and set aside.

Combine water, butter, and cocoa in a heavy saucepan; bring to a boil, stirring constantly. Stir into flour mixture; add buttermilk, eggs, and vanilla. Pour into a greased and floured 13- x 9- x 2-inch baking pan. Bake at 350° for 30 minutes or until a wooden pick inserted in center comes out clean. Prick cake at 1-inch intervals with a fork; spread with Chocolate Candy Frosting. Yield: 15 servings.

Chocolate Candy Frosting:

½ cup butter or margarine
¼ cup plus 2 tablespoons evaporated milk
¼ cup cocoa
1 (16-ounce) package powdered sugar, sifted
1 teaspoon vanilla extract
½ cup chopped pecans or walnuts

Combine butter, milk, and cocoa in a heavy saucepan; bring to a boil, stirring constantly. Stir in sugar; return to a boil, stirring constantly. Immediately remove from heat. Add vanilla and pecans; stir constantly 3 to 5 minutes or until frosting begins to lose its gloss. Yield: enough for one 13- x 9- x 2-inch cake.

FUDGY PEANUT BUTTER CAKE

2 cups all-purpose flour
2 cups sugar
1 teaspoon baking soda
1 cup water
1 cup butter or margarine
¼ cup cocoa
½ cup buttermilk
2 eggs, slightly beaten
1 teaspoon vanilla extract
1 cup creamy peanut butter
1 tablespoon vegetable oil
¼ cup plus 1 tablespoon butter or margarine
3 tablespoons cocoa
¾ teaspoon vanilla extract
3 to 5 tablespoons buttermilk
2½ cups sifted powdered sugar

Combine flour, sugar, and soda; mix well, and set aside.

Combine water, 1 cup butter, and ¼ cup cocoa in a heavy saucepan; bring to a boil, stirring constantly. Gradually stir into flour mixture. Stir in ½ cup buttermilk, eggs, and 1 teaspoon vanilla. Pour into a greased and floured 13- x 9- x 2-inch baking pan; bake at 350° for 30 minutes or until a wooden pick inserted in center comes out clean. Cool in pan.

Combine peanut butter and oil; mix well. Spread on cooled cake.

Combine ¼ cup plus 1 tablespoon butter and 3 tablespoons cocoa in a small saucepan; cook over low heat, stirring constantly, until butter melts and mixture is smooth. Remove from heat; add remaining ingredients. Beat until thick enough to spread; spread over peanut butter mixture. Yield: 15 servings.

CHOCOLATE-NUT CUPCAKES

⅓ cup shortening
1 cup sugar
1 egg
2 cups all-purpose flour
½ teaspoon salt
2½ teaspoons baking powder
¾ cup milk
1 teaspoon vanilla extract
1 (6-ounce) package semisweet chocolate morsels
½ cup chopped walnuts
1 (16½-ounce) can milk chocolate frosting

Cream shortening; gradually add sugar, beating at medium speed of an electric mixer until light and fluffy. Add egg, beating well. Combine flour, salt, and baking powder; add to creamed mixture, and mix well. Add milk, vanilla, chocolate morsels, and nuts; mix well.

Spoon batter into lightly greased muffin pans, filling two-thirds full. Bake at 375° for 20 minutes. Remove from pan; cool completely. Frost with chocolate frosting. Yield: 1½ dozen.

MARBLE CHOCOLATE CHIP CUPCAKES

1 (8-ounce) package cream cheese, softened
1½ cups sugar, divided
1 egg, slightly beaten
⅛ teaspoon salt
1 (6-ounce) package semisweet chocolate morsels
1½ cups all-purpose flour
1 teaspoon baking soda
½ teaspoon salt
¼ cup cocoa
1 cup water
½ cup vegetable oil
1 tablespoon vinegar
1 teaspoon vanilla extract

Combine cream cheese and ½ cup sugar; beat until smooth. Add egg, ⅛ teaspoon salt, and chocolate morsels, stirring well. Set aside.

Combine flour, remaining 1 cup sugar, soda, ½ teaspoon salt, and cocoa; stir until blended. Add water, oil, vinegar, and vanilla; stir until batter is smooth. Spoon batter into paper-lined muffin pans, filling half full. Spoon a tablespoonful of cream cheese mixture into center of each cupcake. Bake at 350° for 25 to 30 minutes or until done. Remove from pan; cool. Yield: 1½ dozen cupcakes.

CHOCOLATE CHIP CHEESECAKE

1 cup vanilla wafer crumbs
¼ cup butter, melted
2 (8-ounce) packages cream cheese, softened
¾ cup sugar
1 (8-ounce) carton commercial sour cream, divided
4 eggs
1 teaspoon vanilla extract
1 (6-ounce) package semisweet chocolate morsels
½ cup sugar
1½ teaspoons lemon juice
1½ teaspoons vanilla extract
Additional semisweet chocolate morsels (optional)

Combine wafer crumbs and butter, mixing well. Press mixture into bottom of a 9-inch springform pan; set aside.

Beat cream cheese at low speed of an electric mixer until light and fluffy; gradually add ¾ cup sugar and ½ cup sour cream, mixing well. Add eggs, one at a time, beating well after each addition. Stir in 1 teaspoon vanilla and 1 package chocolate morsels. Spoon into prepared pan. Bake at 325° for 1 hour. Cool at room temperature on a wire rack for 20 minutes.

Combine remaining sour cream, ½ cup sugar, lemon juice, and 1½ teaspoons vanilla, mixing well; gently spread over top of cheesecake. Bake at 475° for 5 minutes. Cool to room temperature on a wire rack; refrigerate 8 hours. Remove sides of springform pan; sprinkle additional chocolate morsels around top edge and in center of cheesecake, if desired. Yield: one 9-inch cheesecake.

MARBLE MINT CHEESECAKE

3 tablespoons graham cracker crumbs
1 (16-ounce) carton cream-style cottage cheese
2 (8-ounce) packages cream cheese, softened
1½ cups sugar
4 eggs, slightly beaten
1 (16-ounce) carton commercial sour cream
½ cup butter, melted
⅓ cup cornstarch
¾ teaspoon peppermint extract
8 (1-ounce) squares semisweet chocolate
1 (8-ounce) carton frozen whipped topping, thawed
1 (8-ounce) jar chocolate fudge topping
2 tablespoons créme de menthe syrup

Grease a 9-inch springform pan. Coat bottom and sides of pan with graham cracker crumbs, and set aside.

Place cottage cheese in container of electric blender, and process until smooth;

set aside. Beat cream cheese at low speed of an electric mixer until smooth; add cottage cheese, sugar, and eggs, beating well. Add next 4 ingredients, beating at low speed of electric mixer.

Place chocolate in top of double boiler; bring water to a boil. Reduce heat to low; cook until chocolate melts. Remove from heat, and add 1½ cups of cream cheese mixture; blend thoroughly.

Pour half of remaining cream cheese mixture into prepared pan, and top with half of chocolate mixture. Repeat layers. Gently cut through batter in zigzag fashion in several places. Bake at 325° for 1 hour and 15 to 20 minutes. Turn oven off, and allow cheesecake to cool in oven for 2 hours. Remove; cool to room temperature on a wire rack. Chill several hours.

Remove sides of springform pan. Pipe whipped topping over top of cheesecake. Combine chocolate topping and créme de menthe syrup. To serve, drizzle chocolate topping mixture over each slice. Yield: one 9-inch cheesecake.

BLACK FOREST CHEESECAKE

1½ cups chocolate wafer crumbs
¼ cup butter or margarine, melted
3 (8-ounce) packages cream cheese, softened
1½ cups sugar
4 eggs
⅓ cup kirsch or other cherry-flavored liqueur
4 (1-ounce) squares semisweet chocolate
½ cup commercial sour cream
Whipped cream
Maraschino cherries with stems

Combine chocolate wafer crumbs and butter, mixing well; firmly press into bottom and 1 inch up sides of a 9-inch springform pan.

Beat cream cheese at low speed of an electric mixer until light and fluffy; gradually add sugar, mixing well. Add eggs, one at a time, beating well after each addition. Stir in kirsch, and mix until blended. Pour into prepared pan. Bake at 350° for 1 hour. Cool to room temperature on a wire rack.

Place chocolate in top of a double boiler; bring water to a boil. Reduce heat to low; cook until chocolate melts. Cool slightly. Stir in sour cream. Spread chocolate mixture evenly over top. Chill thoroughly. Garnish with whipped cream and cherries. Yield: one 9-inch cheesecake.

RICH CHOCOLATE CHEESECAKE

1½ cups chocolate wafer crumbs
¼ teaspoon ground nutmeg
½ cup butter, melted
2 (8-ounce) packages cream cheese, softened
¾ cup sugar
3 eggs
1 (8-ounce) carton commercial sour cream
6 (1-ounce) squares semisweet chocolate, melted
1 tablespoon plus ¾ teaspoon cocoa
1½ teaspoons vanilla extract
½ cup whipping cream, whipped
Additional whipped cream (optional)
Chocolate curls (optional)
Almonds (optional)
Maraschino cherries (optional)

Combine first 3 ingredients, mixing well. Press mixture into bottom of a 9-inch springform pan; chill.

Beat cream cheese at low speed of an electric mixer until light and fluffy; gradually add sugar, mixing well. Add eggs, one at a time, beating well after each addition. Stir in sour cream, melted chocolate, cocoa, and vanilla; mix well. Gently fold in whipped cream; spoon into prepared pan.

Bake at 300° for 1 hour. Turn oven off; allow cheesecake to cool in oven 30 minutes. Open door, and allow cheesecake to cool in oven an additional 30 minutes. Refrigerate 8 hours. Remove sides of springform pan, and garnish with additional whipped cream, chocolate curls, almonds, and cherries, if desired. Yield: one 9-inch cheesecake.

Candies

CREAMY PECAN FUDGE

3 (12-ounce) packages semisweet chocolate morsels
1 (7-ounce) jar marshmallow creme
1 cup butter or margarine
4½ cups sugar
1 (12-ounce) can evaporated milk
1 tablespoon milk
3 to 4 cups chopped pecans

Combine chocolate morsels, marshmallow creme, and butter; set aside.

Combine sugar and milks in a heavy saucepan; bring to a boil. Reduce heat to low; cook 9 minutes, stirring constantly. Pour over chocolate mixture, stirring until chocolate melts and mixture is smooth. Add pecans; stir until well blended.

Spread mixture in a lightly buttered 15- x 10- x 1-inch jellyroll pan. Chill until firm and cut into squares. Cover and store in refrigerator. Yield: 10 dozen.

CREAM CHEESE FUDGE

4 (1-ounce) squares unsweetened chocolate
2 (3-ounce) packages cream cheese, softened
4 cups sifted powdered sugar
½ teaspoon vanilla extract
1 cup chopped pecans or walnuts
Pecan halves

Place chocolate in top of a double boiler; bring water to a boil. Reduce heat to low; cook until chocolate melts.

Combine cream cheese and sugar, beating at low speed of an electric mixer until smooth. Add melted chocolate and vanilla, beating well. Stir in chopped pecans. Press mixture into a lightly greased 8-inch square pan. Chill until firm and cut into squares. Top each square with a pecan half. Store fudge in refrigerator. Yield: about 1½ dozen.

CHOCOLATE-CARAMEL FUDGE

3 cups firmly packed light brown sugar
3 tablespoons all-purpose flour
1½ cups molasses
¾ cup butter or margarine
6 (1-ounce) squares unsweetened chocolate
1½ cups milk
1½ teaspoons vanilla extract
⅓ cup sliced almonds, toasted

Combine first 4 ingredients in a heavy saucepan. Bring to a boil, stirring constantly; reduce heat, and cook 5 minutes. Add chocolate and milk; stir until chocolate melts. Cook over medium heat, stirring frequently, until mixture reaches soft ball stage (234°). Remove from heat, and stir in vanilla.

Pour mixture into a buttered 9-inch square pan; sprinkle with almonds. Cover and chill overnight; cut into squares. Store in refrigerator. Yield: 3 dozen.

PISTACHIO FUDGE

4 cups sugar
2 cups milk
½ cup butter or margarine
¼ teaspoon salt
1 teaspoon vanilla extract
¼ cup finely chopped dry-roasted pistachios
Candied red and green cherries

Combine first 4 ingredients in a large Dutch oven. Cook over low heat, stirring constantly, until sugar dissolves. Increase to medium heat and cook, stirring occasionally, until mixture reaches soft ball stage (234°). Remove from heat (do not stir). Cool to lukewarm (110°).

Add vanilla and pistachios; beat with a wooden spoon for 2 to 3 minutes or until mixture is thick and begins to lose its gloss. Pour into a buttered 8-inch square pan. Mark top of warm fudge into 1⅓-inch squares. Decorate each square with candied cherries. Cool and cut into squares. Yield: 3 dozen.

CHERRY-NUT FUDGE

3⅔ cups sifted powdered sugar
½ cup cocoa
½ cup butter or margarine
3 tablespoons milk
1 tablespoon vanilla extract
½ cup chopped candied cherries
½ cup chopped pecans

Combine powdered sugar and cocoa; stir well. Set aside.

Combine butter and milk in a medium saucepan; cook over low heat until butter melts. Remove from heat, and stir in cocoa mixture until smooth. Add vanilla, cherries, and pecans; stir well. Pour mixture into a lightly greased 8-inch square pan; chill until firm. Cut into squares. Yield: about 2½ dozen.

DOUBLE PEANUT FUDGE

2 cups sugar
⅔ cup milk
1 cup marshmallow creme
1 cup creamy peanut butter
1 (6-ounce) package semisweet chocolate morsels
1 teaspoon vanilla extract
½ cup coarsely chopped peanuts

Combine sugar and milk in a heavy saucepan. Cook over medium heat, stirring occasionally, until mixture reaches soft ball stage (234°). Remove from heat; add next 4 ingredients. Stir until mixture is well blended; fold in peanuts. Pour into a buttered 8-inch square pan. Cool and cut into squares. Yield: 3 dozen.

FUDGE SCOTCH RING

1 cup walnut halves
1 (6-ounce) package semisweet chocolate morsels
1 (6-ounce) package butterscotch morsels
1 (14-ounce) can sweetened condensed milk
1 cup coarsely chopped walnuts
½ teaspoon vanilla extract
Red and green candied cherries

Line bottom of a 9-inch pieplate with a 12-inch square of aluminum foil. Place a custard cup in center of pieplate. Arrange 1 cup walnut halves around custard cup, forming a 2-inch wide ring; set aside.

Combine chocolate morsels, butterscotch morsels, and condensed milk in top of a double boiler; bring water to a boil. Reduce heat to low, and cook, stirring occasionally, until morsels melt and mixture begins to thicken and become smooth. Remove from heat; stir in 1 cup chopped walnuts and vanilla. Chill 1 hour.

Spoon chocolate-butterscotch mixture in mounds over walnut halves; remove custard cup. Decorate with candied cherries. Yield: one 8-inch ring.

ROCKY ROAD FUDGE

1 (12-ounce) package semisweet chocolate morsels
1 (14-ounce) can sweetened condensed milk
2 tablespoons butter or margarine
2 cups dry-roasted peanuts
1 (10½-ounce) package miniature marshmallows

Place chocolate morsels, milk, and butter in top of a double boiler; bring to a boil. Reduce heat to low; cook until chocolate and butter melt, stirring constantly. Remove from heat, and stir in peanuts and marshmallows. Spread mixture into a wax paper-lined 13- x 9- x 2-inch baking pan. Chill at least 2 hours. Cut into 1½-inch squares. Store in refrigerator. Yield: about 4 dozen.

CHOCOLATE FUDGE

2½ cups sugar
1 (5-ounce) can evaporated milk
2 (1-ounce) squares unsweetened chocolate
2 tablespoons light corn syrup
Dash of salt
2 tablespoons butter
1 teaspoon vanilla extract
1 cup chopped pecans or walnuts

Combine first 5 ingredients in a Dutch oven. Cook over low heat, stirring constantly, until sugar dissolves.

Continue to cook, stirring often until mixture reaches soft ball stage (234°). Remove from heat; add butter and vanilla (do not stir). Cool to lukewarm (110°).

Add pecans; beat with a wooden spoon until mixture is thick and begins to lose its gloss (2 to 3 minutes). Pour into a buttered 8-inch square pan. Mark warm fudge into 1⅓-inch squares. Cool and cut into squares. Yield: 3 dozen.

CHOCOLATE-NUT FUDGE LOG

1⅓ cups sugar
¼ teaspoon salt
2 tablespoons cocoa
¾ cup milk
1 tablespoon light corn syrup
2 tablespoons butter or margarine
1 teaspoon vanilla extract
½ cup finely chopped pecans

Combine sugar, salt, and cocoa in a heavy saucepan; mix well. Gradually stir in milk and syrup. Cook over medium heat, stirring occasionally, until mixture reaches soft ball stage (234°). Remove from heat; stir in butter and vanilla. Pour into a buttered 15- x 10- x 1-inch jellyroll pan; cool 10 minutes.

With buttered hands, knead candy occasionally for 10 to 15 minutes or until cool enough to hold its form. Shape into a 12- x 1¼-inch rope; roll in pecans. wrap in buttered plastic wrap. Cool at room temperature for 1 hour or until completely cooled. Cut into ½-inch slices. Yield: 2 dozen.

CREAMY DARK FUDGE

3 (6-ounce) packages semisweet chocolate morsels
1 (14-ounce) can sweetened condensed milk
1½ teaspoons vanilla extract
⅓ cup chopped pecans

Combine chocolate morsels and condensed milk in a heavy saucepan. Cook over low heat until chocolate melts, stirring constantly. Remove from heat, and stir in vanilla.

Spread chocolate mixture in a lightly greased 8-inch square pan. Sprinkle with pecans. Chill 2 to 3 hours or until firm; cut into squares. Cover and store in refrigerator. Yield: 2 dozen.

TIGER BUTTER

1 pound white chocolate
1 (12-ounce) jar chunky peanut butter
1 pound semisweet chocolate, melted

Combine white chocolate and peanut butter in top of a double boiler; bring water to a boil. Reduce heat to low, and cook, stirring constantly, until chocolate melts. Spread mixture into a wax paper-lined 15- x 10- x 1-inch jellyroll pan.

Pour semisweet chocolate over peanut butter mixture, and swirl through with a knife. Chill until firm. Cut into 1½- x 1-inch pieces. Store in refrigerator. Yield: about 6 dozen.

AMARETTO DESSERT TRUFFLES

12 (1-ounce) squares semisweet chocolate
½ cup butter or margarine
½ cup whipping cream
¼ cup amaretto
Finely chopped almonds or cocoa

Melt chocolate squares in a heavy saucepan over low heat, stirring until smooth. Remove chocolate from heat; add butter 1 tablespoon at a time, stirring until melted.

Add whipping cream and amaretto to chocolate mixture, stirring with a wire whisk. Return to heat, and cook 1 minute or until mixture is thickened and smooth, stirring constantly.

Cover and chill chocolate mixture at least 8 hours or until firm enough to shape.

Shape chocoloate mixture into 1-inch balls; roll in chopped almonds or cocoa. Cover and store in refrigerator. Yield: about 3½ dozen.

ALMOND TRUFFLES

3 tablespoons butter or margarine, softened
½ cup sifted powdered sugar
6 (1-ounce) squares semisweet chocolate, finely grated
3 tablespoons white crème de cacao
24 whole almonds, toasted
½ cup finely chopped almonds

Cream butter; gradually add sugar, beating well at medium speed of an electric mixer. Add chocolate and crème de cacao; beat until mixture is blended. Cover and chill 1 hour.

Shape mixture into 1-inch balls, inserting one whole almond into center of each; roll in chopped almonds. Cover and chill at least 8 hours. Yield: about 2 dozen.

CHOCOLATE-RUM TRUFFLES

1 (6-ounce) package semisweet chocolate morsels
3 tablespoons unsalted butter
3 tablespoons powdered sugar
2 tablespoons whipping cream
1 tablespoon rum
Cocoa

Melt chocolate morsels in a heavy saucepan over low heat, stirring until smooth. Add butter and powdered sugar, stirring until sugar dissolves. Remove from heat.

Stir whipping cream and rum into chocolate mixture. Pour mixture into a bowl; cover and refrigerate for 2 hours or until firm enough to shape.

Shape mixture into 1-inch balls; roll in cocoa. Freeze about 1 hour. Store in an airtight container in refrigerator. Yield: 15 truffles.

CHOCOLATE DROPS

2 (16-ounce) packages powdered sugar, sifted
1½ cups sweetened condensed milk
½ cup butter or margarine, melted
1 teaspoon vanilla extract
2 cups chopped pecans
1 cup flaked coconut
1 (12-ounce) package semisweet chocolate morsels
3 tablespoons shortening

Combine sugar, sweetened condensed milk, butter, and vanilla; stir until smooth. Stir in pecans and coconut. Roll mixture into 1-inch balls, and chill at least 1 hour.

Combine chocolate and shortening in top of a double boiler; bring water to a boil. Reduce heat to low; cook until chocolate melts. Place several candy balls in chocolate mixture; roll with spoon to coat evenly. Remove from mixture with a wooden pick or spoon, allowing excess chocolate to drain. Place on wax paper to cool. Repeat procedure until all candy balls are coated. Cover and store in refrigerator. Yield: 9 dozen.

PROCESSOR CHOCOLATE VELVETS

12 ounces milk chocolate candy
¼ cup unsalted butter
¾ cup whipping cream, scalded
1½ tablespoons crème de cacao or Kahlúa
Chocolate sprinkles or finely chopped pecans

Position knife blade in food processor bowl. Break chocolate into pieces, and place in bowl; process until finely chopped.

Heat butter to 110°. With processor running, add butter and hot whipping cream through feed chute; continue processing 1 minute. Stir in crème de cacao. Pour mixture into a bowl; cover and chill at least 8 hours.

Shape mixture into ¾-inch balls, and roll in chocolate sprinkles or chopped pecans. Freeze 1 hour or until firm. Store in refrigerator. Yield: 3 dozen.

CHOCOLATE BALLS

1 tablespoon cocoa
½ cup powdered sugar
¼ cup bourbon
1 tablespoon light corn syrup
½ cup finely ground pecans or walnuts
1¼ cups finely crushed vanilla wafers
Powdered sugar

Sift cocoa and sugar together; set aside. Combine bourbon and corn syrup in a bowl; stir in cocoa mixture, pecans, and vanilla wafers.

Roll mixture into 1-inch balls; roll each in powdered sugar. Store in a covered container. Yield: 1½ dozen.

CHOCOLATE MARBLES

2 cups (9½ ounces) amaretti almond cookie crumbs
¾ cup butter, softened
⅓ cup amaretto or other almond-flavored liqueur
1½ cups (9 ounces) semisweet chocolate morsels

Combine first 3 ingredients, stirring well; chill. Shape into ¾-inch balls.

Place chocolate in top of a double boiler; bring water to a boil. Reduce heat to low; cook until chocolate melts. Dip each ball into melted chocolate; chill 30 minutes or until chocolate hardens. Store in an airtight container in refrigerator. Yield: about 5 dozen.

CHOCOLATE RUM BALLS

1 (6-ounce) package semisweet chocolate morsels
1 (7-ounce) jar marshmallow creme
1 tablespoon imitation rum extract
3 cups crisp rice cereal
½ cup shredded coconut
½ cup chopped pecans

Place chocolate in top of a double boiler; bring water to a boil. Reduce heat to low; cook until chocolate melts. Cool.

Combine melted chocolate, marshmallow creme, and rum extract; stir well. Add cereal, coconut, and pecans, stirring gently to blend. Shape into 1-inch balls. Chill until firm. Yield: about 4½ dozen.

Note: Rum balls may be rolled in additional coconut or pecans, if desired.

OLD-FASHIONED MILLIONAIRES

1 (14-ounce) package caramels
3 to 4 tablespoons milk
2 cups pecan pieces
Butter or margarine
1 tablespoon shortening
1 (12-ounce) package semisweet chocolate morsels

Melt caramels in milk over low heat; stir in pecans. Drop by teaspoonfuls onto buttered wax paper. Chill. Melt shortening and chocolate morsels in a heavy saucepan over low heat. Remove from heat; dip candy into chocolate, and return to wax paper. Chill. Yield: 3½ dozen.

MOCHA-BOURBON BALLS

12 (1-ounce) squares semisweet chocolate
½ cup butter
⅓ cup sugar
½ cup whipping cream
¼ cup bourbon
1 tablespoon instant coffee granules
2 cups ground pecans, divided
¾ cup chocolate wafer crumbs

Combine chocolate, butter, and sugar in top of a double boiler; bring water to a boil. Reduce heat to low; cook until chocolate and butter melt. Remove from heat; stir in cream, bourbon, coffee granules, and 1 cup pecans. Cover and chill until firm.

Combine remaining cup of pecans and wafer crumbs; stir well. Shape chocolate mixture into 1-inch balls and roll in crumb mixture. Store in refrigerator. Yield: about 5 dozen.

CHOCOLATE-COVERED RAISINS

1 (6-ounce) package semisweet chocolate morsels
¼ cup dark corn syrup
2 tablespoons powdered sugar
1½ teaspoons vanilla extract
2 cups raisins

Combine chocolate morsels and corn syrup in top of a double boiler; bring water to a boil. Reduce heat to low; cook until chocolate melts, stirring constantly. Remove from heat, and stir in powdered sugar, vanilla, and raisins. Drop by half-teaspoonfuls onto wax paper; chill. Store in refrigerator. Yield: about 5½ dozen.

PEANUT BUTTER CREAMS

¼ cup powdered sugar
½ cup sweetened condensed milk
1 cup creamy peanut butter
1 (6-ounce) package semisweet chocolate morsels
½ cup chocolate sprinkles

Combine sugar, condensed milk, and peanut butter in a medium mixing bowl; stir until well blended. Stir in chocolate morsels, and chill until firm. Shape into ¾-inch balls, and roll in chocolate sprinkles. Chill until firm. Yield: 6 to 7 dozen.

MIXED RAISIN CANDY

4 cups sugar
2 cups whipping cream
2 tablespoons light corn syrup
1 (9-ounce) package raisins
2 cups chopped pecans or walnuts
1 cup flaked coconut
2½ cups semisweet chocolate morsels
¼ cup plus 1½ teaspoons shortening

Combine first 3 ingredients in a heavy saucepan; stir well. Bring to a boil, stirring often, until mixture reaches soft ball stage (234°). Remove from heat; cover and chill 1 to 2 hours. Stir in raisins, pecans, and coconut; shape into 1-inch balls.

Combine chocolate and shortening in top of a double boiler; bring water to a boil. Reduce heat to low; cook until chocolate melts. Place several candy balls in chocolate mixture; coat evenly. Remove with a wooden pick or spoon, allowing excess chocolate to drain off. Place on wax paper to cool. Repeat procedure until all candy balls are coated. Cover and store in refrigerator. Yield: 8 dozen.

KENTUCKY COLONELS

½ cup butter, softened
3 tablespoons sweetened condensed milk
⅓ cup plus 2 teaspoons bourbon
7½ cups powdered sugar
½ cup finely chopped pecans
1 (6-ounce) package semisweet chocolate morsels
1 tablespoon shortening
Pecan halves

Combine butter, condensed milk, and bourbon in a large mixing bowl; add sugar, and knead until mixture is blended and does not stick to hands. Knead in chopped pecans. Shape into 1-inch balls.

Combine chocolate morsels and shortening in top of a double boiler; bring water to a boil. Reduce heat to low; cook until chocolate melts.

Using a wooden pick, dip each ball of candy into chocolate mixture, allowing excess chocolate to drain off. Place on wax paper and gently press a pecan half on each. Yield: about 6 dozen.

CHOCOLATE BRITTLE

2 cups butter
2 cups sugar
¼ cup plus 2 tablespoons water
12 (1.05-ounce) milk chocolate candy bars
3 cups chopped pecans

Combine butter, sugar, and water in a Dutch oven; stir well. Cook over low heat, stirring occasionally, until candy reaches hard crack stage (300°). Lightly butter 2 12-inch pizza pans. Remove sugar mixture from heat and immediately pour into pans, spreading to edges of pans.

Place chocolate in top of a double boiler; bring water to a boil. Reduce heat to low, and cook until chocolate melts. Spread chocolate over brittle; sprinkle pecans evenly on top. Press pecans into chocolate. Cool until chocolate is firm. Break candy into pieces. Yield: about 4 pounds.

BUTTER-NUT CRUNCHIES

1 cup sugar
½ cup butter or margarine
¼ cup water
½ teaspoon salt
1½ cups walnuts, finely chopped and divided
1 (12-ounce) package semisweet chocolate morsels

Combine sugar, butter, water, and salt in a heavy saucepan; stir well. Bring to a boil; cook, stirring occasionally, until mixture reaches soft crack stage (285°). Stir in ½ cup walnuts. Pour into a buttered 15- x 10- x 1-inch jellyroll pan, spreading to about ¼-inch thickness. Cool.

Melt chocolate morsels in a heavy saucepan over low heat, stirring constantly; spread half of chocolate over cooled candy. Sprinkle with ½ cup walnuts; lightly press walnuts into chocolate. Cool until firm. Invert candy; repeat procedure with remaining chocolate and walnuts. Cool; break into pieces. Store in an airtight container. Yield: about 1 pound.

WHITE CHOCOLATE SALTIES

1 pound white chocolate
2 tablespoons shortening
3 cups pretzel sticks
1 cup salted Spanish peanuts

Combine chocolate and shortening in top of a double boiler; bring water to a boil. Reduce heat to low; cook until chocolate melts. Pour chocolate mixture into a large mixing bowl. Stir in pretzels and peanuts; spread into a buttered 15- x 10- x 1-inch jellyroll pan. Chill 20 minutes or until firm; break into pieces. Store in an airtight container. Yield: 1½ pounds.

CHOCOLATE-COVERED PRETZELS

1 (5.75-ounce) package milk chocolate morsels
2 tablespoons shortening
24 (3-inch) pretzels

Combine chocolate morsels and shortening in top of a double boiler; bring water to a boil. Reduce heat to low; cook until chocolate melts, stirring occasionally. Remove double boiler from heat, leaving chocolate mixture over hot water.

Dip each pretzel in chocolate; allow excess to drain. Place on wax paper-lined cookie sheets; chill until firm. Arrange pretzels between layers of wax paper in an airtight container; store in a cool place. Yield: 2 dozen.

ALMOND CRUNCH

2 cups butter
2 cups sugar
2 cups finely chopped almonds, toasted and divided
1 pound milk chocolate

Melt butter in a Dutch oven; add sugar, and cook over medium-high heat until mixture comes to a boil. Reduce heat to medium, and boil 5 minutes, stirring frequently. Add 1 cup almonds and cook, stirring constantly, until mixture reaches hard crack stage (300°). Remove from heat, and immediately pour onto two buttered aluminum foil-covered cookie sheets, spreading to about ¼-inch thickness. Cool until candy is hard.

Place chocolate in top of a double boiler; bring water to a boil. Reduce heat to low, and cook until chocolate melts. Working quickly, spread half of chocolate over cooled candy; sprinkle ½ cup almonds evenly on top. Lightly press almonds into chocolate. Chill until firm. Invert candy onto foil, and repeat procedure.

When firm, break candy into pieces. If stored in refrigerator, allow candy to stand at room temperature 5 minutes before serving. Yield: about 3¾ pounds.

Cookies

CHOCOLATE-PEANUT COOKIES

1 cup butter or margarine, softened
1½ cups sugar
2 eggs
2 teaspoons vanilla extract
2 cups all-purpose flour
⅔ cup cocoa
¾ teaspoon baking soda
½ teaspoon salt
1 cup finely chopped peanuts

Cream butter; gradually add sugar, beating at low speed of an electric mixer until light and fluffy. Stir in eggs and vanilla.

Combine flour, cocoa, soda, and salt; add to creamed mixture, beating well. Stir in peanuts.

Drop dough by teaspoonfuls onto ungreased cookie sheets. Bake at 350° for 12 to 14 minutes. Remove to wire racks to cool completely. Yield: about 5½ dozen.

CHOCOLATE-NUT CHEWS

1½ cups sugar
½ cup cocoa
½ cup evaporated milk
⅓ cup butter or margarine
⅓ cup peanut butter
1½ cups quick-cooking oats, uncooked
½ cup chopped pecans or walnuts
1 teaspoon vanilla extract

Combine sugar, cocoa, milk, and butter in a heavy saucepan. Cook over medium heat, stirring constantly, until mixture reaches a slow boil (mixture will bubble around sides). Cook 2 additional minutes, stirring constantly.

Remove from heat; add peanut butter, and stir until smooth. Stir in oats, pecans, and vanilla. Drop by tablespoonfuls onto wax paper; cool. Yield: about 4½ dozen.

CHOCOLATE CHIP COOKIES

½ cup butter or margarine, softened
½ cup sugar
¼ cup firmly packed dark brown sugar
1 egg
1 teaspoon vanilla extract
1½ cups all-purpose flour
½ teaspoon baking soda
¼ teaspoon salt
1 (6-ounce) package semisweet chocolate morsels
½ cup chopped pecans

Cream butter; gradually add sugar, beating at low speed of an electric mixer until light and fluffy. Add egg and vanilla; beat well. Combine flour, soda, and salt; add to creamed mixture, beating well. Stir in chocolate morsels and pecans.

Drop dough by heaping teaspoonfuls onto ungreased cookie sheets. Bake at 350° for 10 to 12 minutes. Cool slightly on cookie sheets; remove to wire racks to cool completely. Yield: 4 dozen.

CHOCOLATE DROP COOKIES

½ cup shortening
1 cup firmly packed brown sugar
1 egg, beaten
2 (1-ounce) squares semisweet chocolate, melted
1 teaspoon vanilla extract
1⅔ cups sifted cake flour
½ teaspoon baking soda
½ teaspoon salt
½ cup milk
½ cup chopped pecans or walnuts
Chocolate-Coffee Frosting

Cream shortening; gradually sugar, beating at low speed of an electric mixer until light and fluffy. Add egg, chocolate, and vanilla; beat well.

Combine flour, soda, and salt; add to creamed mixture alternately with milk, stirring well. Stir in pecans.

Drop dough by teaspoonfuls, about 1½ inches apart, onto greased cookie sheets. Bake at 350° for 10 to 12 minutes or until done. Remove to wire racks and frost with Chocolate-Coffee Frosting while still warm. Yield: about 4 dozen.

Chocolate-Coffee Frosting:

¼ cup plus 2 tablespoons cocoa
¼ cup plus 2 tablespoons hot coffee
¼ cup plus 2 tablespoons butter or margarine, melted
1 teaspoon vanilla extract
3 cups sifted powdered sugar

Combine first 4 ingredients; blend until smooth. Add powdered sugar, stirring well. Yield: enough for about 4 dozen.

CHOCOLATE CHIP-OATMEAL COOKIES

1 cup butter or margarine, softened
¾ cup sugar
¾ cup firmly packed brown sugar
2 eggs
1 teaspoon vanilla extract
1½ cups all-purpose flour
1 teaspoon baking soda
½ teaspoon baking powder
½ teaspoon salt
2 cups quick-cooking oats, uncooked
1 (12-ounce) package semisweet chocolate morsels
1 cup chopped pecans

Cream butter; gradually add sugar, beating at low speed of an electric mixer until light and fluffy. Add eggs and vanilla; beat well. Combine flour, soda, baking powder, and salt; add to creamed mixture, beating well. Stir in remaining ingredients.

Drop dough by heaping teaspoonfuls onto ungreased cookie sheets; bake at 375° for 8 to 10 minutes. Cool slightly on cookie sheets; remove to wire racks to cool completely. Yield: about 7½ dozen.

DELUXE CHOCOLATE CHIP COOKIES

1 cup butter or margarine, softened
2 cups firmly packed brown sugar
2 eggs
1 teaspoon vanilla extract
2 cups all-purpose flour
½ teaspoon baking powder
2 cups crisp rice cereal
1 (6-ounce) package semisweet chocolate morsels
1 cup shredded coconut
1 cup chopped pecans or walnuts

Cream butter; add sugar, beating at low speed of an electric mixer until light and fluffy. Add eggs and vanilla; beat well.

Combine flour and baking powder; add to creamed mixture. Add remaining ingredients, stirring well.

Drop dough by heaping teaspoonfuls onto lightly greased baking sheets. Bake at 350° for 10 to 12 minutes or until lightly browned. Remove to wire racks to cool completely. Yield: about 7½ dozen.

NATURE'S CHOCOLATE CHIP COOKIES

1 cup butter or margarine, softened
¾ cup firmly packed brown sugar
¾ cup sugar
2 eggs
1 teaspoon vanilla extract
1¼ cups all-purpose flour
1 cup whole wheat flour
½ teaspoon baking powder
1 teaspoon baking soda
¼ teaspoon salt
1 (12-ounce) package semisweet chocolate morsels
½ cup salted sunflower kernels
¼ cup sesame seeds

Cream butter; gradually add sugar, beating at low speed of an electric mixer until light and fluffy. Add eggs and vanilla; beat well. Combine flour, baking powder, soda, and salt; add to creamed mixture, beating well. Stir in remaining ingredients.

Drop dough by heaping teaspoonfuls onto lightly greased cookie sheets. Bake at 375° for 8 to 10 minutes. Cool slightly on cookie sheets; remove to wire racks to cool completely. Yield: 5 dozen.

GIANT CHOCOLATE CHIP COOKIES

1 cup butter or margarine, softened
1 cup firmly packed brown sugar
½ cup sugar
2 eggs
2¼ cups all-purpose flour
1 teaspoon baking soda
½ teaspoon salt
1 teaspoon vanilla extract
1½ cups semisweet chocolate morsels
¾ cup chopped pecans

Cream butter; gradually add sugar, beating at low speed of an electric mixer until light and fluffy. Add eggs, and beat until blended.

Combine flour, soda, and salt. Add to creamed mixture, stirring well. Stir in vanilla, chocolate morsels, and pecans.

Divide mixture into thirds. Spoon each third onto an ungreased cookie sheet, spreading into an 8½-inch circle. Bake at 375° for 12 to 14 minutes or until lightly browned. Gently remove cookies to wire racks to cool completely. Yield: three 10-inch cookies.

CHOCOLATE-MINT CHIP COOKIES

2 (1-ounce) squares unsweetened chocolate
½ cup butter or margarine, softened
1 cup sugar
2 eggs
½ teaspoon vanilla extract
2 cups all-purpose flour
1 teaspoon baking powder
⅛ teaspoon salt
6 ounces mint chips, cut into small pieces

Place chocolate in top of a double boiler; bring water to a boil. Reduce heat to low; cook until chocolate melts. Set aside to cool slightly.

Cream butter; gradually add sugar, beating at medium speed of an electric mixer. Add eggs, one at a time, beating well after each addition. Stir in vanilla.

Combine flour, baking powder, and salt; add to creamed mixture, beating well. Stir in chocolate; mix well. Stir in mint chips.

Drop dough by rounded teaspoonfuls onto lightly greased cookie sheets. Bake at 350° for 8 to 10 minutes. Cool slightly on cookie sheets; remove to wire racks to cool completely. Yield: 5 dozen.

ORANGE-CHOCOLATE COOKIES

½ cup shortening
1 (3-ounce) package cream cheese, softened
½ cup sugar
1 egg, beaten
1 teaspoon vanilla extract
1 teaspoon grated orange rind
1 cup all-purpose flour
½ teaspoon salt
1 (6-ounce) package semisweet chocolate morsels

Combine first 4 ingredients in a large bowl; beat at low speed of an electric mixer until smooth and creamy. Add vanilla and orange rind; beat well. Combine flour and salt; add to creamed mixture, beating well. Stir in chocolate morsels.

Drop dough by heaping teaspoonfuls onto ungreased cookie sheets; bake at 350° for 15 minutes or until edges just begin to brown. Remove to wire racks to cool completely. Yield: 3 dozen.

CHOCOLATE CRISPY COOKIES

½ cup butter or margarine, softened
1 cup sugar
1 egg
1 teaspoon vanilla extract
1¼ cups all-purpose flour
½ teaspoon baking soda
¼ teaspoon salt
2 cups crisp rice cereal
1 (6-ounce) package semisweet chocolate morsels

Cream butter; gradually add sugar, beating at low speed of an electric mixer until light and fluffy. Add egg and vanilla; beat well. Combine flour, soda, and salt; add to creamed mixture, beating well. Stir in rice cereal and chocolate morsels.

Drop dough by heaping teaspoonfuls onto lightly greased cookie sheets. Bake at 350° for 13 minutes. Cool slightly on cookie sheets; remove to wire racks to cool completely. Yield: 3½ dozen.

NUGGET COOKIES

1 cup butter, softened
¾ cup sugar
¾ cup firmly packed brown sugar
2 eggs
2½ cups all-purpose flour
1 teaspoon baking soda
1 teaspoon salt
2 teaspoons vanilla extract
1 (6-ounce) package semisweet chocolate morsels
1 cup chopped pecans
2 cups seedless raisins

Cream butter; gradually add sugar, beating at low speed of an electric mixer until light and fluffy. Add eggs, one at a time, beating well after each addition. Combine flour, soda, and salt; add to creamed mixture, beating 1 minute. Stir in vanilla, chocolate morsels, pecans, and raisins.

Drop dough by teaspoonfuls onto lightly greased cookie sheets. Bake at 375° for 10 to 12 minutes or until golden brown. Remove to wire racks to cool completely. Yield: about 2½ dozen.

CHOCOLATE MACAROONS

1 (18.5-ounce) package devil's food cake mix with pudding
1 cup flaked coconut, toasted
½ cup regular oats, uncooked and toasted
¾ cup butter or margarine, melted
2 teaspoons vanilla extract
2 eggs, slightly beaten
6 (1.45-ounce) milk chocolate candy bars, broken into squares
¾ cup flaked coconut

Combine first 6 ingredients; chill 30 minutes. Drop dough by heaping teaspoonfuls 2 inches apart on ungreased cookie sheets. Bake at 350° for 10 minutes. Immediately top each cookie with one chocolate square; spread to frost. Sprinkle cookies with coconut. Yield: about 6 dozen.

FORGET 'EM COOKIES

2 egg whites
Dash of salt
¾ cup sugar
1 teaspoon vanilla extract
1 (6-ounce) package semisweet chocolate morsels
1 cup chopped pecans

Preheat oven to 350°. Beat egg whites (at room temperature) at high speed of an electric mixer until foamy; add salt. Gradually add sugar, 1 tablespoon at a time, beating until stiff peaks form.

Fold vanilla, chocolate morsels, and pecans into beaten egg whites. Drop by teaspoonfuls onto aluminum foil-lined cookie sheets. Place in oven, and immediately turn off heat. Do not open oven door for at least 8 hours. Carefully remove from aluminum foil. Yield: about 3 dozen.

CHEWY CHOCOLATE COOKIES

1½ cups butter or margarine, softened
1 cup sugar
1 cup firmly packed brown sugar
3 eggs
2 teaspoons vanilla extract
4½ cups all-purpose flour
2 teaspoons baking soda
½ teaspoon salt
1 cup chopped pecans
1 (6-ounce) package semisweet chocolate morsels

Cream butter; gradually add sugar, beating at low speed of an electric mixer until light and fluffy. Add eggs and vanilla, beating well.

Combine flour, soda, and salt; add to creamed mixture, beating just until blended. Stir in chopped pecans and chocolate morsels.

Shape dough into 3 long rolls, 2 inches in diameter. Wrap each roll in wax paper, and freeze at least 8 hours.

Unwrap rolls, and cut into ¼-inch slices; place on ungreased cookie sheets. Bake at 350° for 12 to 14 minutes or until lightly browned. Remove to wire racks to cool completely. Yield: about 7 dozen.

JUMBO CHOCOLATE SNAPPERS

1 (6-ounce) package semisweet chocolate morsels
⅔ cup shortening
½ cup sugar
1 egg
¼ cup corn syrup
1¾ cups all-purpose flour
2 teaspoons baking soda
¼ teaspoon salt
1 teaspoon ground cinnamon
Sugar

Place chocolate morsels in top of a double boiler; bring water to a boil. Reduce heat to low; cook until chocolate melts. Remove from heat.

Cream shortening; gradually add ½ cup sugar, beating at low speed of an electric mixer until light and fluffy. Add chocolate, egg, and corn syrup, beating well.

Combine flour, soda, salt, and cinnamon; add to creamed mixture, beating just until blended.

Shape dough into balls, using about 3 tablespoons dough for each ball, and roll in sugar. Place on ungreased cookie sheets about 2½ inches apart; bake at 350° for 18 minutes. Cool on cookie sheets 2 minutes. Remove to wire racks to cool completely. Yield: about 14 jumbo cookies.

Note: For smaller cookies, use 1 tablespoon dough. Bake at 350° for 15 minutes. Yield: about 3½ dozen.

CHOCOLATE SNOWBALL COOKIES

¼ cup butter or margarine, softened
½ cup sugar
1 egg
1 (1-ounce) square unsweetened chocolate, melted
1 teaspoon vanilla extract
1½ cups all-purpose flour
½ teaspoon baking powder
¼ teaspoon salt
Snowy Glaze

Cream butter; gradually add sugar, beating at low speed of an electric mixer until light and fluffy. Add next 3 ingredients, beating well.

Combine flour, baking powder, and salt; gradually add to creamed mixture, beating just until smooth. Chill 1 to 2 hours.

Shape dough into 1-inch balls. Place on greased cookie sheets, and bake at 350° for 12 minutes. Remove to wire racks to cool completely. Dip tops of cookies in Snowy Glaze. Store in an airtight container. Yield: about 3 dozen.

Snowy Glaze:

1 cup sifted powdered sugar
1 tablespoon plus 2 teaspoons milk
½ teaspoon vanilla extract

Combine all ingredients; beat until smooth. Yield: enough for about 3 dozen.

COCOA KISS COOKIES

1 cup butter or margarine, softened
⅔ cup sugar
1 teaspoon vanilla extract
1⅔ cups all-purpose flour
¼ cup cocoa
1 cup coarsely ground walnuts
1 (9-ounce) package milk chocolate kisses, unwrapped

Cream butter; gradually add sugar, beating at low speed of an electric mixer until light and fluffy. Add vanilla, stirring well. Add flour and cocoa, stirring well. Stir in walnuts. Chill dough 2 hours or until firm.

Wrap 1 tablespoon of dough around each chocolate kiss, and roll to form a ball. Place on ungreased cookie sheets; bake at 375° for 12 minutes. Cool slightly on cookie sheets; remove to wire racks to cool completely. Yield: about 4 dozen.

CHOCOLATE CHIP MELT-AWAYS

1 cup butter or margarine, softened
1 cup vegetable oil
1 cup sugar
1 cup sifted powdered sugar
2 eggs
4 cups all-purpose flour
1 teaspoon baking soda
1 teaspoon cream of tartar
1 teaspoon salt
1 teaspoon vanilla extract
1 (12-ounce) package semisweet chocolate morsels
Additional sugar

Combine first 5 ingredients in a large mixing bowl; beat at low speed of an electric mixer until smooth. Combine flour, soda, cream of tartar, and salt; add to butter mixture, beating until smooth. Stir in vanilla and chocolate morsels. Chill.

Shape dough into 1-inch balls; roll in sugar. Place balls 2 inches apart on ungreased cookie sheets; bake at 375° for 10 to 12 minutes or until lightly browned. Remove to wire racks to cool completely. Yield: about 8½ dozen.

CHOCOLATE-CHERRY COOKIES

1 cup butter or margarine, softened
1 cup sifted powdered sugar
1 egg
¼ teaspoon almond extract
2 (1-ounce) squares semisweet chocolate, melted and cooled
2½ cups all-purpose flour
¼ teaspoon cream of tartar
1 cup red candied cherries, coarsely chopped
½ cup finely chopped pecans

Cream butter; gradually add sugar, beating at low speed of an electric mixer until light and fluffy. Add egg, beating well; stir in almond extract. Stir in melted chocolate, mixing well. Combine flour and cream of tartar; add to creamed mixture, stirring well. Stir in cherries and pecans.

Shape dough into two 10- x 2-inch blocks or rolls. Wrap in plastic wrap; freeze several hours or overnight.

Cut dough into ¼-inch slices; place on ungreased cookie sheets. Bake at 375° for 10 to 12 minutes. Remove to wire racks to cool completely. Yield: 5 dozen.

CHOCOLATE PINWHEEL COOKIES

1 (1-ounce) square unsweetened chocolate
½ cup butter or margarine, softened
¾ cup sugar
1 egg
1 teaspoon vanilla extract
1¼ cups all-purpose flour
¼ teaspoon baking powder
¼ teaspoon salt

Place chocolate in top of a double boiler; bring water to a boil. Reduce heat to low; cook until chocolate melts. Set aside to cool slightly.

Cream butter; gradually add sugar, beating at medium speed of an electric mixer until light and fluffy. Add egg and vanilla, beating well. Combine flour, baking powder, and salt; gradually add to creamed mixture, stirring well. Halve dough; stir melted chocolate into one portion. Cover and chill dough 2 hours.

Roll each portion of dough out to a 12- x 10-inch rectangle on lightly floured plastic wrap. (Dough will be soft.) Invert chocolate dough onto plain dough; peel off plastic wrap. Press chocolate dough firmly with a rolling pin; roll up jellyroll fashion starting with long side. Cover and chill at least 8 hours.

Cut dough with an electric knife into ¼-inch-thick slices; place on lightly greased cookie sheets. Bake at 350° for 12 to 14 minutes. Remove to wire racks to cool completely. Yield: about 4 dozen.

BROWNIE WAFFLE COOKIES

⅓ cup shortening
1 (1-ounce) square unsweetened chocolate
1 egg, beaten
½ cup sugar
2 tablespoons milk
½ teaspoon vanilla extract
¾ cup all-purpose flour
½ teaspoon baking powder
¼ teaspoon salt
1 cup finely chopped pecans, divided

Combine shortening and chocolate in a heavy saucepan. Place over low heat, stirring constantly, until melted; cool. Combine egg, sugar, milk, and vanilla in a bowl. Stir in chocolate mixture.

Combine flour, baking powder, and salt; add to chocolate mixture. Add ⅔ cup pecans, stirring well.

Preheat waffle iron at medium heat. Drop batter by level tablespoonfuls onto iron, about 2 inches apart. Sprinkle with remaining ⅓ cup pecans. Close iron, and bake about 3 minutes or until done. Remove to wire racks to cool completely. Yield: 2 dozen.

CHOCOLATE-MINT SNAPS

4 (1-ounce) squares unsweetened chocolate
1¼ cups shortening
2 cups sugar
2 eggs
⅓ cup corn syrup
2½ tablespoons water
2 teaspoons peppermint extract
1 teaspoon vanilla extract
4 cups all-purpose flour
2 teaspoons baking soda
½ teaspoon salt
¼ cup plus 2 tablespoons sugar

Place chocolate in top of a double boiler; bring water to a boil. Reduce heat to low; cook until chocolate melts.

Cream shortening; gradually add 2 cups sugar, beating at low speed of an electric mixer until light and fluffy. Add melted chocolate, eggs, corn syrup, water, and flavorings; mix well. Combine flour, soda, and salt; add to creamed mixture, beating just until blended.

Shape dough into 1-inch balls, and roll in ¼ cup plus 2 tablespoons sugar. Place on ungreased cookie sheets; bake at 350° for 10 minutes. Cool on cookie sheets 5 minutes; remove to wire racks to cool completely. Yield: 10½ dozen.

CHOCOLATE CHIP BROWNIES

¼ cup butter or margarine, softened
¾ cup sugar
¼ cup light corn syrup
2 eggs, beaten
1 teaspoon vanilla extract
2 (1-ounce) squares unsweetened chocolate, melted
1 cup all-purpose flour
½ teaspoon baking powder
½ teaspoon salt
½ cup semisweet chocolate morsels
½ cup chopped walnuts

Cream butter; gradually add sugar, beating well at low speed of an electric mixer. Add corn syrup, eggs, and vanilla; beat well. Stir in melted chocolate.

Combine flour, baking powder, and salt; stir into creamed mixture. Stir in chocolate morsels and walnuts.

Spread mixture into a lightly greased 9-inch square baking pan. Bake at 350° for 25 to 30 minutes. Cool and cut into 1½-inch squares. Yield: 3 dozen.

AMARETTO BROWNIES

1 cup shortening
4 (1-ounce) squares unsweetened chocolate
2 cups sugar
4 eggs, beaten
2 tablespoons amaretto or other almond-flavored liqueur
1½ cups all-purpose flour
½ teaspoon salt
Amaretto Frosting
3 to 4 tablespoons sliced almonds

Combine shortening and chocolate in a heavy saucepan; cook over low heat, stirring constantly, until melted. Add sugar, stirring well. Remove from heat, and cool. Stir in eggs and amaretto.

Combine flour and salt; add to creamed mixture, stirring well. Pour batter into a lightly greased 13- x 9- x 2-inch baking pan. Bake at 400° for 20 minutes; cool. Frost with Amaretto Frosting. Arrange almonds over top, and cut into 2-inch squares. Yield: about 2 dozen.

Amaretto Frosting:

¼ cup butter or margarine
1 (1-ounce) square unsweetened chocolate
2 tablespoons half-and-half
2½ cups sifted powdered sugar
Dash of salt
2 tablespoons amaretto or other almond-flavored liqueur

Combine butter and chocolate in a heavy saucepan; cook over low heat, stirring constantly, until melted. Stir in half-and-half. Add powdered sugar, salt, and amaretto, stirring until thick enough to spread. Yield: enough for about 2 dozen.

CHOCOLATE-PECAN BROWNIES

2 (1-ounce) squares unsweetened chocolate
½ cup butter or margarine
1 cup sugar
½ cup all-purpose flour
1 teaspoon baking powder
2 eggs
1 teaspoon vanilla extract
1 cup chopped pecans

Combine chocolate and butter in top of a double boiler; bring water to a boil. Reduce heat to low, and cook, stirring constantly, until chocolate melts.

Combine sugar, flour, and baking powder in a mixing bowl; add chocolate mixture, mixing well. Add eggs; mix well. Stir in vanilla and pecans. Pour mixture into a greased 9-inch square baking pan. Bake at 350° for 25 to 30 minutes. Cool and cut into 1½-inch squares. Yield: 3 dozen.

FROSTED COCOA BROWNIES

2 cups sugar
2 cups self-rising flour
1 teaspoon baking soda
¼ cup plus 1 tablespoon cocoa
1 cup butter or margarine
1 cup water
½ cup buttermilk
2 eggs, beaten
1 teaspoon vanilla extract
Frosting (recipe follows)

Combine sugar, flour, soda, and cocoa; stir well, and set aside.

Combine butter and water in a small saucepan; cook over medium heat, stirring occasionally, until butter melts. Pour over flour mixture. Beat at medium speed of an electric mixer about 1 minute. Add buttermilk, eggs, and vanilla; beat just until blended.

Pour into a greased and floured 18- x 12- x 1-inch jellyroll pan. Bake at 400° for 15 to 20 minutes or until a wooden pick inserted in center comes out clean.

Spread frosting over brownies. Cool and cut into 2-inch squares. Yield: 4½ dozen.

Frosting:

1 (16-ounce) package powdered sugar, sifted
Dash of salt
¼ cup cocoa
½ cup butter or margarine
⅓ cup milk
1 teaspoon vanilla extract
1 cup chopped pecans

Combine sugar, salt, and cocoa; stir well, and set aside.

Combine butter and milk in a heavy saucepan. Cook over low heat, stirring occasionally, until butter melts. Pour into cocoa mixture; beat until thick enough to spread. Stir in vanilla and pecans. Yield: enough for 4½ dozen.

CRÈME DE MENTHE BROWNIES

½ cup butter or margarine, softened
1 cup sugar
4 eggs
1 cup all-purpose flour
½ teaspoon salt
1 (16-ounce) can chocolate syrup
1 teaspoon vanilla extract
¼ cup butter or margarine, softened
2 cups sifted powdered sugar
2 tablespoons crème de menthe
1 (6-ounce) package semisweet chocolate morsels
¼ cup butter or margarine

Cream ½ cup butter; gradually add 1 cup sugar, beating at low speed of an electric mixer until light and fluffy. Add eggs, one at a time, beating well after each addition.

Combine flour and salt; add to creamed mixture alternately with chocolate syrup, beginning and ending with flour mixture. Stir in vanilla.

Pour batter into a greased and floured 13- x 9- x 2-inch baking pan. Bake at 350° for 25 to 28 minutes. Cool completely. (Brownies will shrink from sides of pan while cooling.)

Cream ¼ cup butter; gradually add 2 cups powdered sugar and crème de menthe, mixing well. Spread evenly over brownies; chill 1 hour.

Combine chocolate morsels and remaining 1/4 cup butter in top of a double boiler; bring water to a boil. Reduce heat to low; cook until chocolate melts. Spread over brownies; chill 1 hour. Cut into 2- x 1½-inch bars. Yield: about 3 dozen.

CHOCOLATE DREAM SQUARES

½ cup butter or margarine
¼ cup plus 1 tablespoon cocoa
¼ cup sugar
1 egg, slightly beaten
1 teaspoon vanilla extract
1 cup flaked coconut
½ cup chopped pecans
2 cups graham cracker crumbs
Custard filling (recipe follows)
1 (6-ounce) package semisweet chocolate morsels
1 tablespoon butter or margarine

Combine first 4 ingredients in top of a double boiler; bring water to a boil. Reduce heat to low; cook until mixture thickens, stirring constantly. Remove from heat. Add vanilla, coconut, pecans, and cracker crumbs; mix well. Press mixture into a 9-inch square pan; chill 15 minutes.

Spread custard filling over chocolate. Chill 30 minutes or until custard mixture becomes firm.

Combine chocolate morsels and butter in a small saucepan; cook over low heat, stirring until chocolate melts. Spread over custard filling. Cool and cut into 1½-inch squares. Cover and store in refrigerator. Yield: 3 dozen.

Custard Filling:

¼ cup butter or margarine, softened
3 tablespoons milk
2 tablespoons vanilla instant pudding mix
2 cups sifted powdered sugar

Cream butter; add milk and pudding mix, beating until well blended. Add powdered sugar, and mix well. Yield: 1 cup.

BLACK WALNUT BROWNIES

½ cup butter or margarine, softened
1 cup sugar
2 eggs, beaten
1 teaspoon vanilla extract
¼ teaspoon salt
⅔ cup all-purpose flour
2 (1-ounce) squares unsweetened chocolate, melted
⅔ cup black walnuts, chopped

Cream butter; gradually add sugar, beating at low speed of an electric mixer until light and fluffy. Add eggs, vanilla, salt, and flour; mix well. Stir in chocolate and nuts. Pour into a greased 8-inch square baking pan. Bake at 325° for 20 minutes or until done. Cut into 2-inch squares. Yield: about 1½ dozen.

CHOCOLATE CHIP-TOFFEE GRAHAMS

11 whole graham crackers (4½- x 2¼-inches), broken into squares
1 cup butter or margarine
1 cup sugar
1 teaspoon ground cinnamon
½ cup finely chopped pecans
1 (6-ounce) package semisweet chocolate mini-morsels

Arrange graham cracker squares in a single layer in a 15- x 10- x 1-inch jellyroll pan. Combine butter and sugar in a saucepan. Bring to a boil over medium heat, stirring constantly until butter melts; boil 2 minutes. Remove from heat, and stir in cinnamon and pecans. Pour mixture evenly over crackers; spread to edges of pan, covering crackers completely. Bake at 350° for 10 to 12 minutes.

Remove from oven, and sprinkle with chocolate morsels. Cool in pan 5 minutes; carefully separate and transfer cookies to wax paper-lined cookie sheets using a spatula. Refrigerate until chocolate hardens. Store cookies, layered between pieces of wax paper, in airtight containers in refrigerator. Yield: about 2 dozen.

BUTTERSCOTCH-MARSHMALLOW BROWNIES

½ cup butterscotch morsels
¼ cup butter or margarine
¾ cup all-purpose flour
⅓ cup firmly packed brown sugar
1 teaspoon baking powder
¼ teaspoon salt
1 egg, slightly beaten
½ teaspoon vanilla extract
1 cup semisweet chocolate morsels
1 cup miniature marshmallows
½ cup chopped pecans

Combine butterscotch morsels and butter in a small saucepan. Cook over medium heat, stirring occasionally, until morsels melt; set aside.

Combine next 4 ingredients; add butterscotch mixture, egg, and vanilla, mixing well. Stir in chocolate morsels, marshmallows, and pecans. Spread mixture in a greased 9-inch square baking pan. Bake at 350° for 20 to 25 minutes. (Brownies will have a chewy texture.) Cool and cut into 1½-inch squares. Yield: 3 dozen.

CHOCOLATE TEA BROWNIES

5 (1-ounce) squares unsweetened chocolate
⅔ cup butter or margarine
5 eggs
2½ cups sugar
2 teaspoons vanilla extract
½ teaspoon salt
1¼ cups all-purpose flour
1½ cups chopped pecans
Chocolate frosting (recipe follows)
Pecan halves

Combine chocolate and butter in a medium saucepan. Cook over low heat until chocolate melts.

Combine eggs, sugar, vanilla, and salt; beat at medium speed of an electric mixer until blended. Stir in flour, chopped pecans, and chocolate mixture.

Pour batter into a lightly greased 15- x 10- x 1-inch jellyroll pan. Bake at 350° for 25 minutes or until a wooden pick inserted in center comes out clean. Spread with chocolate frosting while brownies are still warm. Cut into 2-inch squares; top each with a pecan half. Yield: about 3 dozen.

Chocolate Frosting:

¼ cup plus 2 tablespoons butter or margarine
1½ (1-ounce) squares unsweetened chocolate, melted
3 tablespoons half-and-half
3 cups sifted powdered sugar
2 tablespoons kirsch or other cherry-flavored liqueur

Combine first 3 ingredients in a medium saucepan; cook until butter and chocolate melt. Remove from heat, and stir in sugar and kirsch; beat until thick enough to spread. Yield: enough for about 3 dozen.

ALMOND-CHOCOLATE BARS

1 (8-ounce) package cream cheese, softened
¾ cup butter or margarine, softened
¾ cup sugar
2 cups all-purpose flour
½ teaspoon baking powder
1 teaspoon vanilla extract
1 (6-ounce) package semisweet chocolate morsels
½ cup sliced almonds, toasted

Combine cream cheese and butter in a mixing bowl; beat well at low speed of an electric mixer. Gradually add sugar, beating until light and fluffy. Combine flour and baking powder; add to creamed mixture, beating well. Stir in vanilla. Spread mixture evenly in an ungreased 13- x 9- x 2-inch baking pan. Bake at 375° for 15 minutes.

Sprinkle chocolate morsels immediately over baked layer; let stand 5 minutes or until chocolate melts. Spread chocolate evenly, to edge of pan. Sprinkle with almonds. Cool and cut into 3- x 1-inch bars. Yield: 3 dozen.

CHOCOLATE CHIP-PEANUT BUTTER BROWNIES

⅓ cup butter or margarine, softened
½ cup peanut butter
½ cup sugar
½ cup firmly packed brown sugar
2 eggs
1 cup all-purpose flour
1 teaspoon baking powder
¼ teaspoon salt
1 teaspoon vanilla extract
1 (6-ounce) package chocolate morsels

Cream butter and peanut butter. Gradually add sugar, beating at low speed of an electric mixer until light and fluffy. Add eggs, one at a time, beating well after each addition.

Combine flour, baking powder, and salt; add to creamed mixture, stirring well. Stir in vanilla and chocolate morsels.

Pour batter into a greased 8-inch square baking pan. Bake at 350° for 30 to 35 minutes. Cool and cut into 2-inch squares. Yield: about 1½ dozen.

HEAVENLY HASH BROWNIES

2 (1-ounce) squares unsweetened chocolate
½ cup butter or margarine
2 eggs
1 cup sugar
½ cup all-purpose flour
Chocolate-Marshmallow Frosting

Combine chocolate and butter in top of a double boiler; bring water to a boil. Reduce heat to low; cook, stirring constantly, until chocolate melts. Cool.

Combine eggs and sugar; beat at medium speed of an electric mixer just until blended. Add chocolate mixture and flour; beat just until smooth. Pour into a greased 9-inch square baking pan. Bake at 350° for 25 to 30 minutes. Cool completely. Spread with Chocolate-Marshmallow Frosting. Cool and cut into 1½-inch squares. Yield: 3 dozen.

Chocolate-Marshmallow Frosting:

2 (1-ounce) squares unsweetened chocolate
½ cup butter
1½ cups sifted powdered sugar
¼ cup egg substitute
1 teaspoon vanilla extract
2 cups miniature marshmallows
1 cup chopped pecans or walnuts

Combine chocolate and butter in top of a double broiler; bring water to a boil. Reduce heat to low; cook, stirring constantly, until chocolate melts. Cool.

Combine powdered sugar, egg substitute, vanilla, and chocolate mixture in a bowl; beat at medium speed of an electric mixer until smooth. Stir in marshmallows and pecans. Yield: enough for 3 dozen.

CHOCOLATE CHIP SCOTCH BARS

⅓ cup shortening
⅓ cup butter or margarine, softened
½ cup sugar
½ cup firmly packed brown sugar
1 egg
1 teaspoon vanilla extract
1½ cups all-purpose flour
½ teaspoon salt
1 (6-ounce) package semisweet chocolate morsels
1 (6-ounce) package butterscotch morsels
½ cup chopped pecans

Cream shortening and butter; gradually add sugar, beating at low speed of an electric mixer until light and fluffy. Beat in egg and vanilla. Add remaining ingredients, and mix well. Pour into an ungreased 13- x 9- x 2-inch baking pan. Bake at 375° for 20 to 25 minutes. Cut into 2- x 1-inch bars. Yield: 4½ dozen.

CHOCOLATE-CINNAMON SQUARES

- 2 cups all-purpose flour
- 1 teaspoon baking powder
- 1 cup sugar
- 1 tablespoon ground cinnamon
- ½ cup butter or margarine, softened
- ½ cup shortening
- 1 egg, slightly beaten
- 1 egg, separated
- ⅓ cup sugar
- 1 teaspoon ground cinnamon
- 1 (6-ounce) package semisweet chocolate morsels
- ½ cup chopped pecans

Combine first 4 ingredients in a large bowl. Add butter, shortening, egg, and egg yolk, mixing well. Press evenly into a lightly greased 15- x 10- x 1-inch jellyroll pan. Beat egg white slightly, and brush over mixture.

Combine ⅓ cup sugar, 1 teaspoon cinnamon, chocolate morsels, and pecans; sprinkle over bottom layer. Bake at 350° for 25 minutes. Cool and cut into 2-inch squares. Yield: about 3 dozen.

MERINGUE-CHOCOLATE CHIP BARS

- 1½ cups all-purpose flour
- ½ cup firmly packed brown sugar
- ½ cup butter or margarine, melted
- 1 (6-ounce) package semisweet chocolate morsels
- 1½ cups chopped pecans
- 3 egg whites
- 1 cup firmly packed brown sugar

Combine flour and ½ cup brown sugar in a small bowl. Stir in butter, blending well. Press mixture into an ungreased 13- x 9- x 2-inch baking pan. Sprinkle with chocolate morsels and pecans.

Beat egg whites (at room temperature) at high speed of an electric mixer until foamy. Gradually add 1 cup brown sugar, beating until stiff peaks form. Spread meringue over chocolate and pecans. Bake at 375° for 18 to 20 minutes. Cool and cut into 3- x 1-inch bars. Yield: 3 dozen.

BY-CRACKY BARS

- ¾ cup shortening
- 1 cup sugar
- 2 eggs
- 1¾ cups all-purpose flour
- 1 teaspoon salt
- ¼ teaspoon baking soda
- ⅓ cup milk
- 1 teaspoon vanilla extract
- 1 (1-ounce) square unsweetened chocolate, melted
- ¾ cup chopped walnuts
- 8 to 9 double graham crackers
- 1 (6-ounce) package semisweet chocolate morsels

Cream shortening and sugar. Add eggs, one at a time, beating well at low speed of an electric mixer.

Combine flour, salt, and soda; add to creamed mixture alternately with milk, mixing well after each addition. Add vanilla, stirring well.

Place one-third of batter in another bowl, and add unsweetened chocolate and walnuts to this mixture. Spread chocolate mixture in a greased 13- x 9- x 2-inch baking pan. Arrange 8 to 9 double graham crackers over batter.

Add chocolate morsels to remaining two-thirds batter, and drop by spoonfuls over crackers, spreading to cover. Bake at 375° for 25 minutes. Cool and cut into 3- x 1-inch bars. Yield: 3 dozen.

CHOCOLATE CHIP SQUARES

- ¾ cup butter or margarine, softened
- 1 cup firmly packed brown sugar
- 2 cups all-purpose flour
- 1 teaspoon vanilla extract
- 1 (6-ounce) package chocolate morsels
- ¾ cup chopped pecans

Cream butter; gradually add sugar, beating well. Stir in flour and vanilla.

Press into an ungreased 13- x 9- x 2-inch baking pan. Sprinkle with chocolate morsels and pecans. Bake at 350° for 15 to 20 minutes. Cool; cut into 1½-inch squares. Yield: about 4 dozen.

COCONUT-CHOCOLATE CHEWS

1½ cups graham cracker crumbs
½ cup butter or margarine, melted
1 (6-ounce) package semisweet chocolate morsels
1 (6-ounce) package butterscotch morsels
1¼ cups flaked coconut
1 cup chopped pecans
1 (14-ounce) can sweetened condensed milk

Combine crumbs and butter; stir well, and press into a 9-inch square baking pan. Layer chocolate morsels, butterscotch morsels, coconut, and pecans over crumb mixture. Pour milk evenly over top. Bake at 350° for 35 to 40 minutes. Cool and cut into 1½-inch squares. Yield: 3 dozen.

CHOCOLATE-PEPPERMINT SQUARES

½ cup butter or margarine, softened
1 cup sugar
2 eggs
½ cup all-purpose flour
Pinch of salt
2 (1-ounce) squares unsweetened chocolate, melted
½ cup chopped pecans or walnuts
Peppermint Filling
Chocolate Glaze

Cream butter; gradually add sugar, beating at low speed of an electric mixer until light and fluffy. Add eggs, one at a time, beating well after each addition.

Combine flour and salt; add to creamed mixture, beating well. Add chocolate, beating until blended; stir in pecans.

Pour batter into a greased 9-inch square baking pan. Bake at 350° for 20 minutes. Cool (layer will fall while cooling).

Spread Peppermint Filling over layer, and chill (filling will be very thin).

Drizzle chocolate glaze over filling; chill thoroughly. Cut into 1-inch squares. Store in refrigerator. Yield: about 7 dozen.

Peppermint Filling:

1 cup sifted powdered sugar
2 tablespoons butter or margarine, softened
1 tablespoon milk
½ to ¾ teaspoon peppermint extract

Combine all ingredients, beating until smooth. Yield: about ½ cup.

Chocolate Glaze:

2 (1-ounce) squares semisweet chocolate, melted
1 tablespoon butter or margarine, melted

Combine ingredients; stir well. Yield: about ¼ cup.

Desserts

HOT FUDGE PUDDING

1 cup self-rising flour
1¾ cups sugar, divided
¼ cup cocoa, divided
½ cup milk
2 tablespoons butter, melted
1 teaspoon vanilla extract
Pinch of salt
1½ cups hot water
Whipped cream or ice cream (optional)

Combine flour, ¾ cup sugar, and 2 tablespoons cocoa; stir in milk, butter, and vanilla. Pour mixture into a 9-inch square baking pan.

Combine remaining cup of sugar, remaining 2 tablespoons cocoa, and salt; sprinkle over flour mixture. Pour water over top; bake at 350° for 30 minutes. Serve warm with whipped cream or ice cream, if desired. Yield: 6 servings.

CHOCOLATE BREAD PUDDING

3 cups soft breadcrumbs
¼ cup cocoa
½ cup chopped pecans or walnuts
2 eggs
½ cup sugar
3 cups milk
1 teaspoon vanilla extract
¼ teaspoon salt
Whipped cream (optional)

Combine breadcrumbs, cocoa, and pecans, stirring well, set aside.

Beat eggs with a wire whisk until foamy; gradually add sugar, beating well 1 minute. Stir in milk, vanilla, salt, and breadcrumb mixture.

Pour mixture into a lightly greased 1¾-quart casserole. Bake at 350° for 45 to 50 minutes or until set. Serve pudding warm with whipped cream, if desired. Yield: 6 to 8 servings.

CHOCOLATE-ORANGE SOUFFLÉ ROLL

2 (4-ounce) packages sweet baking chocolate
⅓ cup water
1 teaspoon Grand Marnier or other orange-flavored liqueur
8 eggs, separated
1 cup sugar
2 tablespoons cocoa
1 cup whipping cream
3 tablespoons powdered sugar
½ teaspoon vanilla extract
Additional powdered sugar
Semisweet chocolate-dipped orange sections

Grease bottom and sides of an 18- x 12- x 1-inch jellyroll pan with vegetable oil; line with wax paper.

Combine chocolate and water in top of a double boiler; bring water to a boil. Reduce heat to low; cook, stirring occasionally, until chocolate melts. Stir in Grand Marnier; set aside to cool.

Place egg yolks in a large bowl; beat at high speed of an electric mixer until foamy. Gradually add 1 cup sugar, beating until thick and lemon colored. Gradually add chocolate mixture, mixing well.

Beat egg whites (at room temperature) at high speed of an electric mixer until stiff peaks form. Fold whites into chocolate mixture. Pour into jellyroll pan, spreading evenly. Bake at 350° for 20 minutes. Immediately cover with a damp linen towel; cool on a wire rack 20 minutes. Remove towel. Loosen edges of soufflé with a metal spatula; sift cocoa over top.

Place 2 lengths of wax paper (longer than jellyroll pan) over soufflé. Holding both ends of wax paper and pan, quickly invert pan. Remove pan and carefully peel paper from soufflé.

Beat whipping cream until foamy; gradually add 3 tablespoons powdered sugar and vanilla, beating until soft peaks form. Spoon whipped cream mixture evenly over soufflé. Starting at short side, carefully roll up jellyroll fashion, using wax paper to support as you roll.

Carefully slide roll (on wax paper) onto a plate, seam side down. Chill. Sift additional powdered sugar over roll. Garnish with semisweet chocolate-dipped orange sections. Trim away excess wax paper around sides of roll. Yield: 12 servings.

Note: The chocolate roll is fragile and may crack or break during rolling.

HOT CHOCOLATE SOUFFLÉ

1 teaspoon sugar
2 tablespoons butter or margarine
2 tablespoons all-purpose flour
¾ cup milk, scalded
Pinch of salt
2 (1-ounce) squares unsweetened chocolate
½ cup sugar
2 tablespoons brewed coffee
3 egg yolks, beaten
½ teaspoon vanilla extract
4 egg whites
Sweetened whipped cream
Grated chocolate (optional)

Lightly butter bottom of a 1½-quart soufflé dish; sprinkle with 1 teaspoon sugar, and set aside.

Melt 2 tablespoons butter in a heavy saucepan over low heat; add flour, stirring until smooth. Cook 1 minute, stirring constantly. Gradually add milk; cook over medium heat, stirring constantly, until thickened and bubbly. Stir in salt. Remove from heat; set aside.

Combine 2 squares chocolate, ½ cup sugar, and coffee in top of a double boiler; bring water to a boil. Reduce heat to low; cook until chocolate melts. Stir chocolate mixture into sauce.

Gradually stir one-fourth of hot mixture into yolks; add to remaining hot mixture, stirring constantly. Stir in vanilla.

Beat egg whites (at room temperature) at high speed of an electric mixer until stiff peaks form. Gently fold into chocolate mixture. Carefully spoon into prepared soufflé dish. Bake at 350° for 50 minutes or until puffed and set. Serve immediately with whipped cream and grated chocolate, if desired. Yield: 6 servings.

CHOCOLATE-MOCHA SOUFFLÉ ROLL

6 eggs, separated
½ cup sugar
½ cup cocoa
½ teaspoon vanilla extract
Dash of salt
¼ cup sugar
Powdered sugar
Mocha Cream Filling

Grease a 15- x 10- x 1-inch jellyroll pan with vegetable oil, and line with wax paper. Grease wax paper lightly; set aside.

Place egg yolks in a large bowl, and beat at high speed of an electric mixer until foamy; gradually add ½ cup sugar, beating until mixture is thick and lemon colored. Add cocoa, vanilla, and salt; beat at low speed of an electric mixer until blended.

Beat egg whites (at room temperature) at high speed of an electric mixer until foamy. Gradually add ¼ cup sugar, 1 tablespoon at a time, beating until stiff peaks form. Fold egg whites into cocoa mixture. Spread batter evenly in prepared pan; bake at 375° for 15 minutes.

Sift powdered sugar in a 15- x 10-inch rectangle on a towel. When soufflé is done, immediately loosen from sides of pan, and turn out onto sugar. Peel off wax paper. Starting at long side, roll up soufflé and towel together; cool on a wire rack, seam side down.

Unroll and remove towel. Spread Mocha Cream Filling over soufflé, and reroll. Place on a serving plate, seam side down. Chill. Before serving, sift additional powdered sugar over roll. Yield: 10 servings.

Mocha Cream Filling:

1½ cups whipping cream
½ cup sifted powdered sugar
¼ cup cocoa
2 teaspoons instant coffee granules
1 teaspoon vanilla extract

Beat whipping cream until foamy; gradually add powdered sugar, cocoa, and coffee granules, beating until soft peaks form. Stir in vanilla. Yield: about 3¼ cups.

RUM-FLAVORED POTS DE CRÉME

2 cups half-and-half
1 tablespoon sugar
6 egg yolks, slightly beaten
8 (1-ounce) squares semisweet chocolate, coarsely chopped
2 tablespoons dark rum
Whipped cream
Slivered almonds, toasted

Combine first 3 ingredients in a heavy saucepan; cook over medium heat 12 minutes or until mixture reaches 160°, stirring constantly. Add chocolate, stirring until smooth. Stir in rum.

Pour into serving dishes. Chill at least 8 hours. Garnish with whipped cream and almonds. Yield: 6 servings.

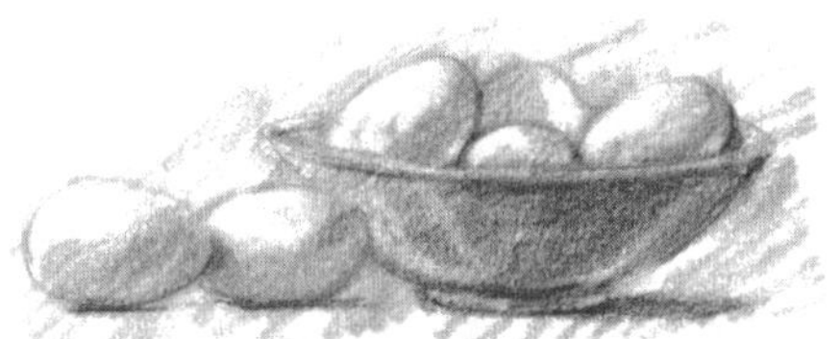

CHOCOLATE-RUM DESSERT

1 (6-ounce) package semisweet chocolate morsels
1¼ cups whipping cream, divided
¼ cup egg substitute
2 tablespoons light rum
¼ teaspoon almond extract
¼ teaspoon ground nutmeg
Additional whipped cream
Chocolate curls

Combine chocolate and ¼ cup whipping cream in a heavy saucepan; cook over low heat, stirring until chocolate is melted. Remove from heat.

Beat egg substitute well. Gradually stir one-fourth of chocolate into egg substitute; add to remaining chocolate, stirring constantly. Stir in rum, almond extract, and nutmeg. Let cool completely.

Beat 1 cup cream at high speed of an electric mixer until stiff peaks form; fold into cooled chocolate mixture. Spoon into cordial glasses or demitasse cups. Chill. Garnish with additional whipped cream and chocolate curls. Yield: 4 servings.

CHOCOLATE-ALMOND VELVET

1/3 cup chocolate syrup
1/3 cup sweetened condensed milk
1/4 teaspoon vanilla extract or almond extract
1 cup whipping cream, whipped
1/4 cup toasted slivered almonds

Combine chocolate syrup, condensed milk, and vanilla; chill.

Fold whipped cream into chocolate mixture; pour into individual serving dishes. Sprinkle each serving with almonds. Cover and freeze 3 to 4 hours or until firm. Yield: 6 to 8 servings.

AMARETTO-CHOCOLATE MOUSSE

1 (6-ounce) package semisweet chocolate morsels
18 whole blanched almonds
1/2 cup amaretto or other almond-flavored liqueur
2 envelopes unflavored gelatin
1/4 cup water
4 egg yolks
1/3 cup sugar
2 cups milk
3 cups whipping cream, whipped
2 (3-ounce) packages ladyfingers, split

Place chocolate in top of a double boiler; bring water to a boil. Reduce heat to low; cook until chocolate melts.

Dip larger end of each almond into melted chocolate, and place almonds on a wax paper-lined cookie sheet. Chill until chocolate is firm.

Gradually stir amaretto into remaining melted chocolate using a wire whisk; set aside.

Combine gelatin and water in a medium saucepan; let stand 1 minute. Beat egg yolks slightly; stir into gelatin mixture using a wire whisk. Add sugar and milk, mixing well. Cook over low heat, stirring constantly until slightly thickened and mixture reaches 160°. Remove from heat; stir in chocolate mixture. Cover and chill until consistency of unbeaten egg white.

Set aside in refrigerator 1 cup whipped cream for garnish. Gently fold remaining whipped cream into chocolate mixture.

Line bottom and sides of a 9-inch springform pan with ladyfingers. Spoon chocolate mixture into pan. Cover and chill 4 hours or until firm.

Place dessert on a large serving platter, and remove rim from pan. Garnish mousse as desired with the remaining cup of whipped cream and chocolate-dipped almonds. Cut into wedges to serve. Yield: 12 to 14 servings.

CHOCOLATE-ORANGE MOUSSE

1 (4-ounce) package sweet baking chocolate
4 (1-ounce) squares semisweet chocolate
1/4 cup Grand Marnier or other orange-flavored liqueur
2 cups whipping cream
1/2 cup sifted powdered sugar
Additional whipped cream (optional)
Chocolate curls (optional)

Combine 8 ounces of chocolate and Grand Marnier in a heavy saucepan; cook over low heat until chocolate melts, stirring constantly. Remove from heat, and cool to lukewarm.

Beat whipping cream until foamy; gradually add powdered sugar, beating until soft peaks form. Gently fold about one-fourth of whipped cream into chocolate mixture; fold in remaining whipped cream.

Spoon into individual serving dishes. Cover and chill until ready to serve. Garnish mousse with additional whipped cream and chocolate curls, if desired. Yield: 6 servings.

BRANDY-CHOCOLATE MOUSSE

1 (6-ounce) package semisweet chocolate morsels
¼ cup plus 1 tablespoon butter
½ cup egg substitute
2 tablespoons brandy
¼ cup sifted powdered sugar
1 cup whipping cream
Additional whipped cream

Melt chocolate and butter in a heavy saucepan over low heat, stirring until smooth. Remove from heat; stir one-fourth of chocolate mixture into egg substitute, beating constantly with a wire whisk. Stir egg substitute mixture into remaining chocolate mixture, beating constantly with a wire whisk. Cool. Stir in brandy and sugar; beat well.

Beat 1 cup whipping cream at high speed of an electric mixer until stiff peaks form; gently fold cream into cooled chocolate mixture. Spoon into stemmed glasses or individual serving dishes; cover and chill until set. Garnish with additional whipped cream, if desired. Yield: 6 servings.

MOCHA ALASKA DESSERT

¾ cup vanilla wafer crumbs
¾ cup graham cracker crumbs
½ cup finely chopped pecans
½ cup butter or margarine, melted
2 tablespoons cocoa
½ gallon coffee ice cream, softened
6 (1$\frac{1}{16}$-ounce) English toffee-flavored candy bars, crushed
3 egg whites
½ cup sugar
1 tablespoon Kahlúa

Combine first 5 ingredients. Press mixture evenly into bottom of a 9-inch square pan. Bake at 350° for 8 minutes. Cool.

Combine softened ice cream and crushed candy bars. Spoon over cooled crust; cover and freeze until firm.

Combine egg whites and ½ cup sugar in top of a double boiler. Place over simmering water. Cook, stirring constantly with a wire whisk, 5 minutes or until mixture reaches 160°. Remove from heat. Beat at high speed 3 to 5 minutes or until firm peaks form. Add Kahlúa, mixing well. Spread meringue over top of ice cream mixture, making sure edges are sealed. Bake at 475° for 3 minutes or until lightly browned. Yield: 9 servings.

BROWNIE ALASKAS

1 (15.5-ounce) package fudge brownie mix
1½ pints strawberry ice cream
4 egg whites
¾ cup sugar
½ teaspoon cream of tartar

Prepare brownie mix according to package directions using a 9-inch square baking pan; cool completely. Cut brownies into 3-inch squares.

Arrange brownies on a cookie sheet; top each with a scoop of ice cream. Freeze at least 1 hour.

Combine egg whites, ¾ cup sugar, and cream of tartar in top of a double boiler. Place over simmering water. Cook, stirring constantly with a wire whisk, 5 minutes or until mixture reaches 160°. Remove from heat. Beat at high speed 5 minutes or until firm peaks form.

Remove ice cream-topped brownies from freezer. Spread meringue over ice cream, making sure edges are sealed. Bake at 500° for 2 to 3 minutes or until lightly browned. Yield: 9 servings.

CHOCOLATE-LADYFINGER DESSERT

1 cup cocoa
½ cup sugar
4 eggs, separated
¼ cup water
½ cup butter or margarine, softened
1 cup sifted powdered sugar
1 teaspoon vanilla extract
½ cup chopped walnuts
¾ cup sugar
½ teaspoon cream of tartar
16 ladyfingers, split
1 cup whipping cream
1½ tablespoons powdered sugar
½ teaspoon vanilla extract

Combine cocoa and ½ cup sugar in top of a double boiler; mix well. Stir in egg yolks and ¼ cup water; bring water in bottom of double boiler to a boil. Reduce heat to low; cook, stirring constantly, for 5 minutes. Set aside to cool.

Cream butter, 1 cup powdered sugar, and 1 teaspoon vanilla in a large bowl; beat in cooled cocoa mixture until smooth. Stir in walnuts; set aside.

Combine egg whites, ¾ cup sugar, and cream of tartar in top of a double boiler. Place over simmering water. Cook, stirring constantly, with a wire whisk, 5 minutes or until mixture reaches 160°. Remove from heat. Beat at high speed 5 minutes or until firm peaks form. Fold egg white mixture into cocoa mixture; set aside.

Line bottom and sides of an 8-inch springform pan with ladyfingers, placing rounded sides of ladyfingers toward outside of pan. Spoon chocolate mixture into pan; cover and chill at least 8 hours.

Combine whipping cream, 1½ tablespoons powdered sugar, and ½ teaspoon vanilla; beat at medium speed of an electric mixer until stiff peaks form. Spread over chocolate mixture. Place on a serving plate; remove rim from springform pan. Yield: 6 to 8 servings.

FROZEN MOCHA DESSERT

2 (3-ounce) packages ladyfingers, split
1 cup water
1 tablespoon instant coffee granules
1 (16-ounce) package marshmallows
2 tablespoons cream sherry
3 cups whipping cream
2 (1-ounce) squares semisweet chocolate, grated

Line bottom and sides of a 10-inch springform pan with ladyfingers, placing rounded sides of ladyfingers toward outside of pan. Set aside.

Combine water and coffee in top of a double boiler; bring water to a boil. Reduce heat to low; add marshmallows, and cook until marshmallows melt. Remove from heat; add sherry. Set aside to cool.

Beat whipping cream until soft peaks form. Fold whipped cream into cooled marshmallow mixture; pour into prepared pan. Cover and freeze at least 8 hours.

Place on a serving plate; remove rim from springform pan. Top dessert with grated chocolate. Yield: 14 to 16 servings.

CHOCOLATE DREAM DESSERT

2 dozen ladyfingers, split
¼ cup Kahlúa or other coffee-flavored liqueur
12 (1-ounce) squares semisweet chocolate
2 (8-ounce) packages cream cheese, softened
¾ cup sugar, divided
2 teaspoons vanilla extract
3 egg whites
2 cups whipping cream, whipped
Sweetened whipped cream
Chocolate curls
Maraschino cherries

Line bottom and sides of a 9-inch springform pan with ladyfingers, placing rounded sides of ladyfingers toward outside of pan. Brush cut side of ladyfingers with Kahlúa. Set aside.

Melt chocolate in a heavy saucepan over low heat, stirring until smooth. Remove from heat, and let cool.

Beat cream cheese and ¼ cup sugar at low speed of an electric mixer until light and fluffy. Stir in melted chocolate and vanilla; mix until smooth.

Combine egg whites and remaining ½ cup sugar in top of a double boiler. Place over simmering water. Cook, stirring constantly with a wire whisk, 5 minutes or until mixture reaches 160°. Remove from heat. Beat at high speed 3 to 5 minutes or until firm peaks form. Fold egg whites and whipped cream into chocolate mixture; pour into pan. Cover and chill at least 8 hours.

Place on a serving platter, and remove rim from springform pan. Garnish dessert with whipped cream, chocolate curls, and cherries. Yield: 14 to 16 servings.

LAYERED ICE CREAM DESSERT

3/4 cup chocolate wafer crumbs, divided
1 cup butter or margarine
2 (1-ounce) squares unsweetened chocolate
2 cups sugar
1/2 cup egg substitute
1 1/4 cups whipping cream
1 cup coarsely chopped pecans
1 quart vanilla ice cream, softened

Sprinkle 1/2 cup wafer crumbs in an ungreased 13- x- 9- x 2-inch pan. Set aside.

Combine butter, chocolate, and sugar in a heavy saucepan; cook over low heat until chocolate melts. Remove from heat.

Gradually stir one-fourth of chocolate mixture into egg substitute; add to remaining chocolate mixture, stirring constantly with a wire whisk. Let cool.

Beat whipping cream at high speed of an electric mixer until stiff peaks form; fold into cooled chocolate mixture. Carefully spoon mixture over crumbs, and sprinkle with pecans. Cover and freeze until firm.

Spread ice cream evenly over pecan layer; sprinkle with remaining crumbs. Freeze until firm. Yield: 15 servings.

CHOCOLATE-COFFEE FROZEN DESSERT

2 cups vanilla wafer crumbs, divided
1/4 cup butter or margarine, melted
2 1/2 (1-ounce) squares unsweetened chocolate
1/2 cup butter or margarine
2 cups sugar
1/4 cup egg substitute
1 teaspoon vanilla extract
1 1/4 cups whipping cream
1 cup coarsely chopped pecans
2 quarts coffee ice cream, softened

Combine 1 3/4 cups vanilla wafer crumbs and 1/4 cup butter. Press mixture into a 13- x 9- x 2-inch pan; set aside.

Combine chocolate, 1/2 cup butter, and sugar in a heavy saucepan; cook over low heat until chocolate melts. Remove from heat.

Gradually stir one-fourth of chocolate mixture into egg substitute; add to remaining chocolate mixture, stirring constantly with a wire whisk. Add vanilla; beat 2 minutes at medium speed of an electric mixer. Let cool.

Beat whipping cream at high speed of an electric mixer until stiff peaks form; fold into cooled chocolate mixture. Spread mixture over crumbs; sprinkle with pecans. Cover and freeze until firm.

Spread ice cream over pecan layer; sprinkle with remaining crumbs. Cover and freeze until firm. Yield: 15 servings.

COOL CHOCOLATE-MINT DESSERT

1/2 cup butter or margarine
2 (1-ounce) squares unsweetened chocolate, melted
1 cup sifted powdered sugar
1/2 cup egg substitute
1 cup chopped pecans, divided
1 cup whipping cream, whipped
2 cups crushed chocolate sandwich cookies, divided
8 ounces hard peppermint candy, crushed
1 cup miniature marshmallows
1 cup whipping cream, whipped

Combine butter, chocolate, and sugar in a heavy saucepan; cook over low heat until butter and chocolate melt, stirring constantly. Remove from heat.

Gradually stir one-fourth of chocolate mixture into egg substitute; add to remaining chocolate mixture, stirring constantly. Stir in 1/2 cup pecans, and set aside to cool.

Fold 2 cups of the whipped cream into cooled chocolate mixture; set aside.

Press 1 cup cookie crumbs into bottom of an 8-inch square dish; spread chocolate mixture over crumbs. Chill until firm.

Combine candy, marshmallows, remaining 1/2 cup pecans, and 1/2 cup cookie crumbs; stir well. Gently stir in remaining 2 cups whipped cream. Spread whipped cream mixture over chocolate layer; sprinkle remaining cookie crumbs over top. Serve chilled or frozen. Yield: 9 servings.

CHOCOLATE DREAM CRÊPES

½ cup semisweet chocolate morsels
2 tablespoons butter or margarine
½ cup sifted powdered sugar
¼ cup light corn syrup
2 tablespoons crème de cacao
2 tablespoons water
½ teaspoon vanilla extract
1 quart chocolate ice cream
Chocolate Crêpes
½ cup chopped pecans

Combine chocolate morsels and butter in top of a double boiler; bring water to a boil. Reduce heat to low; cook until chocolate melts. Remove from heat. Add powdered sugar, syrup, crème de cacao, water, and vanilla, stirring until smooth.

Spoon about 3 tablespoons ice cream down center of each Chocolate Crêpe; fold sides over, and place seam side down on serving dishes. Spoon warm chocolate sauce over each; sprinkle with chopped pecans. Yield: 10 servings.

Chocolate Crêpes:

½ cup all-purpose flour
1 tablespoon cocoa
2 teaspoons sugar
Dash of salt
¾ cup milk
¼ teaspoon almond extract
1 egg
2 teaspoons butter or margarine, melted
Vegetable oil

Combine flour, cocoa, sugar, and salt. Add milk and almond extract; beat at low speed of an electric mixer until smooth. Add egg, and beat well; stir in butter. Refrigerate batter 2 hours. (This allows flour particles to swell and soften so that crêpes are light in texture.)

Brush bottom of a 6-inch crêpe pan or heavy skillet with oil; place over medium heat until just hot, not smoking.

Pour 2 tablespoons batter into pan; quickly tilt pan in all directions so batter covers pan in a thin film. Cook 1 minute or until lightly browned.

Lift edge of crêpe to test for doneness. Crêpe is ready for flipping when it can be shaken loose from pan. Flip crêpe, and cook about 30 seconds on other side. (This side is rarely more than spotty brown and is the side on which the filling is placed.)

Place crêpes on a towel to cool. Stack between layers of wax paper to prevent sticking. Repeat until all batter is used. Yield: 10 (6-inch) crêpes.

MOCHA CHIFFON

1 envelope unflavored gelatin
¼ cup cold water
¾ cup milk
⅓ cup semisweet chocolate morsels
3 tablespoons cocoa
2 egg yolks
½ cup sugar
2 teaspoons instant coffee granules
1 teaspoon vanilla extract
2 cups whipping cream, whipped
Additional whipped cream (optional)
Chocolate shavings (optional)

Sprinkle gelatin over water; let stand at least 5 minutes.

Combine milk, chocolate morsels, and cocoa in heavy saucepan; cook over low heat until chocolate melts. Remove chocolate mixture from heat.

Combine egg yolks and sugar in a small mixing bowl, stirring well. Gradually stir about one-fourth of hot mixture into egg yolk mixture; add to remaining hot mixture, stirring constantly.

Add coffee granules to hot mixture. Cook over low heat, stirring constantly, until mixture thickens. Remove from heat and stir in softened gelatin and vanilla. Chill just until mixture is consistency of unbeaten egg white.

Gently fold whipped cream into chocolate mixture. Spoon into a 1-quart casserole; cover and chill until firm. Garnish with additional whipped cream and chocolate shavings, if desired. Yield: 4 to 6 servings.

ROYAL MOCHA FREEZE

2 cups whipping cream
½ cup chocolate syrup
⅓ cup brandy
1 quart coffee ice cream, softened
1 (6-ounce) package semisweet chocolate morsels
¾ cup chopped almonds, toasted
Whipped cream (optional)
Chocolate leaves (optional)
Maraschino cherries (optional)

Combine whipping cream, chocolate syrup, and brandy; beat at low speed of an electric mixer until thickened. Place ice cream in a large plastic or metal freezer container; fold chocolate mixture into ice cream. Stir in chocolate morsels, and almonds. Freeze, uncovered, about 3 hours. Remove from freezer, and stir well. Cover and freeze until firm.

Spoon into parfait glasses and garnish with whipped cream, chocolate leaves, and maraschino cherries, if desired. Yield: about 12 servings.

CHOCOLATE-MINT CUPS

2 (1-ounce) squares unsweetened chocolate, melted
1 cup butter, softened
2 cups sifted powdered sugar
1 cup egg substitute
2 teaspoons vanilla extract
1 teaspoon peppermint extract
12 vanilla wafers, finely crushed
¼ cup finely chopped pecans

Combine chocolate, butter, and sugar in a heavy saucepan; cook over low heat until chocolate melts, stirring frequently. Remove from heat.

Add a small amount of chocolate mixture to egg substitute, stirring constantly with a wire whisk. Add to remaining chocolate mixture, stirring constantly with a wire whisk. Stir in flavorings.

Combine vanilla wafer crumbs and pecans; stir well. Sprinkle half of crumb mixture into 12 ungreased muffin cups.

Spoon chocolate mixture over crumb mixture, and top with remaining crumb mixture. Cover and freeze until firm. To serve, run a knife around edge of each muffin cup, and gently lift out dessert. Serve immediately. Yield: 12 servings.

CHOCOLATE TORTE ROYALE

1 (6-ounce) package semisweet chocolate morsels
Cinnamon Meringue Shell
2 egg yolks
¼ cup water
1 cup whipping cream
¼ teaspoon ground cinnamon
¼ cup sugar
Additional whipping cream
Whole pecans

Place chocolate morsels in top of a double boiler; bring water to a boil. Reduce heat to low; cook until chocolate melts. Cool slightly, and spread 2 tablespoons over bottom of meringue shell (layer will be thin).

Beat egg yolks until thick and lemon colored. Add remaining chocolate and ¼ cup water, beating until thoroughly blended. Cook over medium heat, stirring constantly, until candy thermometer registers 160°, stirring constantly with a wire whisk. Let cool. Cover and chill.

Beat 1 cup whipping cream and cinnamon at low speed of an electric mixer until foamy; gradually add sugar, beating until soft peaks form. Spread half of sweetened whipped cream in meringue shell. Fold remaining whipped cream into chocolate mixture; carefully spread over whipped cream layer. Chill at least 8 hours. Garnish with additional whipped cream and pecans. Yield: 8 servings.

Cinnamon Meringue Shell:

2 egg whites
½ teaspoon vinegar
¼ teaspoon salt
¼ teaspoon ground cinnamon
½ cup sugar

Beat egg whites, vinegar, salt, and cinnamon at high speed of an electric mixer 1 minute. Gradually add sugar, 1 tablespoon at a time, beating until stiff peaks form.

Spoon meringue onto unglazed brown paper. (Do not use recycled paper.) Use a spoon to shape meringue into a circle about 8 inches in diameter, swirling sides to about 1¾-inches high.

Bake at 275° for 1 hour. Turn off oven, and allow meringue to cool in oven 2 hours. Yield: one 8-inch meringue shell.

EASY ICE CREAM BALLS

½ gallon peppermint or vanilla ice cream
14 chocolate sandwich cookies, crushed
2 (1-inch) squares semisweet chocolate
½ cup butter or margarine
1 (5-ounce) can evaporated milk
2 cups sifted powdered sugar
Whipped cream (optional)
Maraschino cherries (optional)

Scoop ice cream into 2½-inch balls. Lightly roll in cookie crumbs. Cover and freeze until firm.

Combine chocolate and butter in top of a double-boiler; bring water to a boil. Reduce heat to low; cook until chocolate melts. Stir in milk and sugar. Cook, stirring constantly, until thickened and smooth.

Arrange ice cream balls in individual serving dishes. Garnish with whipped cream and cherries, if desired. Top with warm sauce just before serving. Yield: 18 ice cream balls.

CHOCOLATE CHUNK-PEANUT BUTTER ICE CREAM

3 eggs
1½ cups sugar
3 (12-ounce) cans evaporated milk
2 tablespoons peanut butter
6 (2.16-ounce) chocolate-covered crispy peanut butter candy bars, crushed
3 cups milk

Combine eggs, sugar, and 2 cans evaporated milk in a heavy saucepan; mix well. Cook over medium heat, stirring constantly, until slightly thickened. Remove from heat; let cool.

Pour mixture into freezer can of a 5-quart hand-turned or electric freezer. Stir in peanut butter, candy, remaining evaporated milk, and 3 cups milk. Freeze according to manufacturer's instructions. Let ripen 1 hour. Yield: 1 gallon.

CHOCOLATE DESSERT SHELLS

⅔ cup semisweet chocolate morsels
2 cups flaked coconut
½ cup chopped pecans or walnuts
Ice cream or fruit

Place chocolate morsels in a heavy saucepan; cook over low heat until chocolate melts. Stir in coconut and pecans.

Line a muffin tin with 8 paper baking cups. Spoon chocolate mixture into cups; press firmly on bottom and sides to form a shell. Chill until hardened.

To serve, gently peel paper cups from chocolate shells. Fill shells with ice cream or fruit. Yield: 8 servings.

Pies

CHOCOLATE MERINGUE PIE

1¼ cups sugar
½ cup cocoa
⅓ cup cornstarch
¼ teaspoon salt
3 cups milk
3 egg yolks
3 tablespoons butter or margarine
1½ teaspoons vanilla extract
1 baked 9-inch pastry shell
Easy Cooked Meringue

Combine sugar, cocoa, cornstarch, and salt in a heavy saucepan, stirring well. Gradually add milk, stirring until blended. Cook over medium heat, stirring constantly, until mixture is thickened and bubbly; boil 1 minute, stirring constantly. Remove from heat.

Beat egg yolks until thick and lemon colored. Gradually stir about one-fourth of hot mixture into yolks; add to remaining hot mixture, stirring constantly. Cook over medium heat 2 minutes, stirring constantly. Remove from heat; stir in butter and vanilla. Immediately pour into pastry shell. Spread Easy Cooked Meringue over filling, sealing to edge of pastry. Bake at 425° for 5 to 7 minutes or until golden brown. Cool. Yield: one 9-inch pie.

Easy Cooked Meringue:

½ cup water
¼ cup plus 2 tablespoons sugar
1 tablespoon cornstarch
3 egg whites
Dash of salt

Combine water, sugar, and cornstarch in a small saucepan; cook over medium heat, stirring constantly, until transparent and thickened. Beat egg whites and salt at high speed of an electric mixer 1 minute. Gradually pour cooked mixture into egg whites in a heavy stream, beating 3 minutes or until stiff peaks form. Yield: enough for one 9-inch pie.

EASY CHOCOLATE PIE

1 cup sugar
3 tablespoons cornstarch
Dash of salt
2 cups milk
3 eggs, separated
1 (1-ounce) square unsweetened chocolate
1 tablespoon butter or margarine
1 teaspoon vanilla extract
1 baked 9-inch pastry shell
½ teaspoon cream of tartar
¼ cup plus 2 tablespoons sugar

Combine 1 cup sugar, cornstarch, and salt in a heavy saucepan; stir well.

Combine milk and egg yolks; beat with a wire whisk 1 to 2 minutes or until frothy. Gradually stir into sugar mixture, mixing well. Cook over medium heat, stirring constantly, until thickened and bubbly. Remove from heat; add chocolate, butter, and vanilla, stirring until chocolate and butter melt. Spoon into pastry shell; set aside.

Beat egg whites and cream of tartar at high speed of an electric mixer 1 minute. Gradually add ¼ cup plus 2 tablespoons sugar, 1 tablespoon at a time, beating until stiff peaks form. Spread meringue over filling, sealing to edge of pastry. Bake at 325° for 20 to 25 minutes or until golden brown. Yield: one 9-inch pie.

FUDGE PIE

¾ cup butter or margarine
3 (1-ounce) squares unsweetened chocolate
3 eggs
1½ cups sugar
¾ cup all-purpose flour
1 teaspoon vanilla extract
¾ cup chopped pecans, toasted and divided
Vanilla ice cream
Chocolate syrup

Melt butter and chocolate in a small saucepan over low heat, stirring often.

Beat eggs at medium speed with an electric mixer 5 minutes. Gradually add sugar, beating until blended. Gradually add chocolate mixture, flour, and vanilla, beating until blended. Stir in ½ cup pecans.

Pour mixture into a lightly greased 9-inch pieplate.

Bake at 350° for 35 to 40 minutes or until center is firm. Cool. Top each serving with vanilla ice cream and chocolate syrup; sprinkle with remaining ¼ cup chopped pecans. Yield: one 9-inch pie.

CHOCOLATE WHIPPED CREAM PIE

2 (1-ounce) squares unsweetened chocolate
¾ cup sugar
Pinch of salt
¼ cup plus 1 tablespoon all-purpose flour
1 (12-ounce) can evaporated milk, divided
2 egg yolks, well beaten
1 cup water
2 cups miniature marshmallows
¼ cup butter or margarine
1 (9-inch) graham cracker crust
1 cup whipping cream
¼ cup sugar
Grated unsweetened chocolate

Place chocolate in top of double boiler; bring water to a boil. Reduce heat to low; cook until chocolate melts. Add ¾ cup sugar, salt, flour, and ⅓ cup evaporated milk, stirring well.

Add a small amount of chocolate mixture to egg yolks, mixing well; add to remaining hot mixture, stirring constantly. Stir in water and remaining evaporated milk. Cook over boiling water until smooth and thickened, stirring constantly. Remove from heat. Add marshmallows and butter, stirring until melted. Cool.

Pour filling into crust. Cover and chill thoroughly. Combine whipping cream and ¼ cup sugar; beat at high speed of an electric mixer until stiff peaks form. Spread over filling, and sprinkle with grated chocolate. Chill. Yield: one 9-inch pie.

CHOCOLATE CREAM PIE WITH CHERRY SAUCE

1½ cups whipping cream
3 (1-ounce) squares unsweetened chocolate, coarsely chopped
¾ cup sugar
2 tablespoons cornstarch
⅛ teaspoon salt
2 eggs, beaten
1½ teaspoons vanilla extract
1 unbaked 9-inch pastry shell
Sifted powdered sugar (optional)
Cherry Sauce

Combine whipping cream and chocolate in a heavy saucepan; cook over low heat, stirring constantly, until mixture is smooth. Set aside.

Combine sugar, cornstarch, and salt in a medium bowl, mixing well; stir in eggs, vanilla, and chocolate mixture. Pour into pastry shell. Bake at 400° for 35 minutes. Cool completely on a wire rack. Sprinkle with powdered sugar, if desired. Serve with Cherry Sauce. Yield: one 9-inch pie.

Cherry Sauce:

¼ cup brandy
1 teaspoon cornstarch
1 (16-ounce) can cherry pie filling

Combine brandy and cornstarch in a small saucepan, stirring until smooth; add pie filling. Cook over medium heat, stirring constantly, until thickened. Yield: about 2¼ cups.

CHOCOLATE-BERRY PIE

1¼ cups graham cracker crumbs
⅓ cup butter or margarine, melted
3 tablespoons sugar
½ cup plus 2 tablespoons semisweet chocolate morsels, divided
1 (8-ounce) package cream cheese, softened
¼ cup firmly packed brown sugar
½ teaspoon vanilla extract
1 cup whipping cream, whipped
1 pint fresh strawberries
1 teaspoon shortening

Combine first 3 ingredients, mixing well; firmly press onto bottom and sides of a lightly greased 9-inch pieplate. Bake at 325° for 10 minutes. Cool completely.

Place ½ cup chocolate morsels in top of a double boiler; bring water to a boil. Reduce heat to low; cook until chocolate melts. Set aside to cool slightly.

Beat softened cream cheese at low speed of an electric mixer until light and fluffy; add brown sugar and vanilla, mixing well. Add cooled chocolate, stirring well. Fold whipped cream into cream cheese mixture; spoon into prepared crust. Chill at least 8 hours.

Set aside 1 strawberry; cut remaining strawberries into thick slices. Arrange slices over filling; place whole strawberry in center.

Combine remaining 2 tablespoons chocolate morsels and shortening in a small saucepan; cook over low heat until chocolate melts. Drizzle over strawberries. Yield: one 9-inch pie.

AMARETTO-CHOCOLATE CREAM PIE

1 cup sugar
⅓ cup cornstarch
¼ teaspoon salt
4 egg yolks
2¾ cups plus 2 tablespoons milk
2 (1-ounce) squares unsweetened chocolate, chopped
¼ cup amaretto or other almond-flavored liqueur
2 teaspoons vanilla extract
1 9-inch baked pastry shell
1 cup whipping cream
1 tablespoon amaretto or other almond-flavored liqueur
¼ cup sifted powdered sugar
Shaved chocolate (optional)

Combine sugar, cornstarch, salt, and egg yolks in a heavy saucepan; stir well. Gradually stir in milk; add chocolate. Cook over medium heat, stirring constantly, until chocolate melts and mixture is thickened and bubbly.

Remove from heat; stir in ¼ cup amaretto and vanilla. Pour into pastry shell. Place a piece of plastic wrap over filling; chill at least 8 hours.

Combine whipping cream, 1 tablespoon amaretto, and powdered sugar; beat at low speed of an electric mixer until soft peaks form. Spread whipped cream mixture over pie; garnish with shaved chocolate, if desired. Yield: one 9-inch pie.

KAHLÚA PIE

1 envelope unflavored gelatin
¼ cup water
2 (1-ounce) squares semisweet chocolate
½ cup sugar
¼ cup water
4 egg yolks
¼ cup Kahúla or other coffee-flavored liqueur
2¼ cups whipping cream
2 tablespoons powdered sugar
1 baked 9-inch pastry shell
Chopped toasted almonds

Sprinkle gelatin over ¼ cup water; set aside for gelatin to soften.

Combine chocolate, ½ cup sugar, and ¼ cup water in top of a double boiler; bring water to a boil. Reduce heat to low; cook until chocolate melts.

Beat egg yolks until thick and lemon colored. Gradually stir about one-fourth of hot chocolate mixture into yolks; add to remaining hot chocolate mixture, stirring constantly. Cook, stirring constantly, until mixture thickens. Remove from heat, and gently stir in gelatin mixture and Kahlúa (mixture will be thin). Chill just until slightly thickened.

Beat whipping cream until foamy; gradually add powdered sugar, beating until soft peaks form. Set aside 1¼ cups whipped cream. Fold remaining whipped cream into chocolate mixture. Spoon mixture into pastry shell; cover and chill until firm. Top with remaining 1¼ cups whipped cream; sprinkle with almonds. Yield: one 9-inch pie.

CHOCOLATE-ALMOND PIE

1 (7-ounce) milk chocolate with almonds candy bar
18 marshmallows
½ cup milk
1 cup whipping cream, whipped
1 baked 9-inch pastry shell

Combine candy bar, marshmallows, and milk in a heavy saucepan. Cook over low heat, stirring occasionally, until melted. Remove from heat; cool. Fold in whipped cream. Pour into pastry shell. Chill at least 8 hours. Yield: one 9-inch pie.

FRENCH SILK PIE

3 egg whites
¼ teaspoon cream of tartar
⅛ teaspoon salt
¾ cup sugar
½ cup chopped pecans
½ teaspoon vanilla extract
1 (4-ounce) bar sweet baking chocolate
3 tablespoons water
1 tablespoon brandy
2 cups whipping cream, divided
Grated sweet chocolate

Beat egg whites (at room temperature), cream of tartar, and salt at high speed of an electric mixer 1 minute. Gradually add sugar, 1 tablespoon at a time, beating until stiff peaks form. Fold in chopped pecans and vanilla.

Spoon meringue into a well-greased 9-inch pieplate. Using a spoon, shape meringue into a shell, swirling sides high. Bake at 300° for 1 hour. Cool.

Combine chocolate and water in a medium saucepan. Cook over low heat, stirring often, until chocolate melts. Cool; stir in brandy. Beat 1 cup whipping cream until stiff peaks form; fold into chocolate mixture. Pour into cooled meringue shell; chill at least 3 hours.

Beat remaining cup of whipping cream until stiff peaks form; spread evenly over top of pie. Garnish with grated chocolate. Yield: one 9-inch pie.

FREEZER MOUSSE PIE

½ cup butter or margarine, softened
¾ cup sugar
2 (1-ounce) squares unsweetened chocolate, melted and cooled
½ cup egg substitute
1 (8-ounce) carton frozen whipped topping, thawed
1 baked 9-inch pastry shell
Whipped cream (optional)
Shaved chocolate (optional)

Cream butter and sugar in a large mixing bowl until light and fluffy; stir in chocolate. Add egg substitute, beating at low speed of an electric mixer 8 minutes. Fold in whipped topping.

Spoon filling into pastry shell. Freeze until firm. Garnish with whipped cream and shaved chocolate, if desired. Yield: one 9-inch pie.

CHOCOLATE-MINT ICE CREAM PIE

20 chocolate sandwich cookies, crushed
¼ cup butter or margarine, softened
1 quart vanilla ice cream, softened
¼ cup plus 2 tablespoons green crème de menthe
2 tablespoons crème de cacao
1 cup whipping cream
2 tablespoons powdered sugar
Chocolate shavings (optional)
Chocolate curls (optional)

Combine chocolate cookie crumbs and butter, stirring well; press into a buttered 9-inch pieplate.

Combine ice cream, crème de menthe, and crème de cacao, stirring until smooth. Spread ice cream mixture evenly over crust; cover and freeze.

Beat whipping cream at high speed of an electric mixer until foamy; gradually add sugar, beating until soft peaks form. Spread whipped cream mixture over pie. Garnish with chocolate shavings and curls, if desired; freeze until firm.

Let stand at room temperature 5 minutes before serving. Yield: one 9-inch pie.

TIPSY MUD PIE

1 (15-ounce) package chocolate sandwich cookies, crushed
¼ cup plus 2 tablespoons butter or margarine, melted
1 banana, thinly sliced
1 tablespoon lemon juice
1 pint chocolate ice cream, softened
½ teaspoon vanilla extract
1 tablespoon instant coffee powder
1 (12-ounce) carton frozen whipped topping, thawed and divided
2 tablespoons brandy
2 tablespoons Kahlúa or other coffee-flavored liqueur
½ cup plus 2 tablespoons chopped pecans
2 tablespoons chocolate syrup

Combine cookie crumbs and butter, stirring well; press into a buttered 10-inch pieplate. Combine sliced banana and lemon juice, tossing gently; drain. Arrange banana in a single layer over chocolate crust. Cover and freeze until firm.

Combine ice cream, vanilla, coffee powder, ¼ cup whipped topping, brandy, Kahlúa, and ½ cup pecans, stirring well. Spread evenly over chocolate crust. Cover and freeze at least 8 hours.

Spread remaining whipped topping over pie; drizzle with chocolate syrup. Sprinkle with remaining 2 tablespoons pecans. Yield: one 10-inch pie.

FROZEN CHOCOLATE PIES

2 (4-ounce) bars sweet baking chocolate
½ cup egg substitute
1 envelope unflavored gelatin
2 tablespoons water
3 cups whipping cream
1 cup powdered sugar
1 teaspoon vanilla extract
Dash of salt
1 cup chopped pecans
2 (6-ounce) chocolate cookie crusts
2 tablespoons chocolate sprinkles

Place chocolate in top of a double boiler; bring water to a boil. Reduce heat to low; cook until chocolate melts. Remove from heat. Stir a small amount of chocolate into egg substitute; add egg mixture to remaining chocolate, stirring constantly with a wire whisk.

Sprinkle gelatin over water; let stand 3 minutes. Add to chocolate mixture, stirring until dissolved.

Combine cream, sugar, vanilla, and salt in a large mixing bowl. Beat at high speed of an electric mixer until firm peaks form. Fold cream mixture and pecans into chocolate mixture; spoon equally into crusts. Sprinkle chocolate sprinkles evenly over each pie. Freeze until firm. Let stand at room temperature 10 minutes before slicing. Yield: two 9-inch pies.

CHOCOLATE-PRALINE PIE

2 eggs
½ cup sugar
½ cup butter or margarine, melted
2 tablespoons praline liqueur
1 (6-ounce) package semisweet chocolate morsels
1 cup chopped pecans
1 unbaked 9-inch pastry shell
Vanilla ice cream (optional)

Combine first 4 ingredients; beat at medium speed of an electric mixer until blended. Stir in chocolate morsels and pecans. Pour into pastry shell. Bake at 350° for 30 minutes. Serve with ice cream, if desired. Yield: one 9-inch pie.

NUTTY CHOCOLATE CHIP PIE

¼ cup plus 2 tablespoons butter or margarine, softened
1 cup sugar
1 teaspoon vanilla extract
2 eggs
½ cup all-purpose flour
1 (6-ounce) package semisweet chocolate morsels
¾ cup chopped pecans
½ cup flaked coconut
1 unbaked 9-inch pastry shell

Cream butter, sugar, and vanilla in a medium mixing bowl, beating at low speed of an electric mixer. Add eggs, and beat well. Stir in flour. Gradually stir in chocolate morsels, pecans, and coconut. Pour mixture into pastry shell. Bake at 350° for 35 to 40 minutes. Yield: one 9-inch pie.

CHOCOLATE-NUT CHESS PIE

1½ cups sugar
3½ tablespoons cocoa
Pinch of salt
1 tablespoon all-purpose flour
1 tablespoon cornmeal
½ cup chopped pecans
3 eggs, beaten
½ cup milk
1 tablespoon vanilla extract
1 unbaked 9-inch pastry shell
Sifted powdered sugar (optional)

Combine first 6 ingredients in a medium bowl; mix well. Combine eggs, milk, and vanilla; stir into sugar mixture, mixing well. Pour into pastry shell. Bake at 350° for 45 to 50 minutes or until set. Cool. Sift powdered sugar over pie, if desired. Yield: one 9-inch pie.

CHOCOLATE PECAN PIE

⅔ cup evaporated milk
2 tablespoons butter or margarine
1 (6-ounce) package semisweet chocolate morsels
2 eggs, beaten
1 cup sugar
2 tablespoons all-purpose flour
¼ teaspoon salt
1 teaspoon vanilla extract
1 cup chopped pecans
1 unbaked 9-inch pastry shell

Combine milk, butter, and chocolate morsels in a small saucepan; cook over low heat, stirring constantly, until chocolate melts. Remove from heat.

Combine eggs, sugar, flour, salt, vanilla, and pecans; stir in chocolate mixture. Pour into pastry shell. Bake at 375° for 35 to 40 minutes. Yield: one 9-inch pie.

Sauces and Frostings

CLASSIC CHOCOLATE SAUCE

2 (1-ounce) squares unsweetened chocolate
¼ cup butter or margarine
1¼ cups sugar
½ teaspoon salt
¾ cup evaporated milk
½ teaspoon vanilla extract

Place chocolate and butter in top of a double boiler; bring water to a boil. Reduce heat to low; cook until chocolate melts. Stir in sugar, salt, and milk. Cook over medium heat, stirring until sugar dissolves and sauce is smooth. Stir in vanilla. Serve warm over ice cream. Store in refrigerator. Yield: 2 cups.

BLENDER CHOCOLATE-CHERRY SAUCE

½ cup pitted fresh sweet cherries
½ cup chocolate syrup

Combine cherries and chocolate syrup in container of an electric blender; process 15 seconds at high speed. Serve over vanilla ice cream. Store in refrigerator. Yield: about 1 cup.

BEST FUDGE SAUCE

1 cup sugar
2 tablespoons cocoa
¼ cup milk
¼ cup whipping cream
2 tablespoons light corn syrup
1 tablespoon butter or margarine
½ tablespoon vanilla extract

Combine sugar and cocoa; stir in milk. Add whipping cream, corn syrup, and butter; mix well. Cook over medium heat, stirring constantly, just until mixture comes to a boil. Reduce heat, and simmer 10 minutes without stirring. Remove from heat; stir in vanilla. Serve warm over ice cream. Store in refrigerator. Yield: 1 cup.

EASY HOT FUDGE SAUCE

3 tablespoons cocoa
1 cup sugar
1 (5-ounce) can evaporated milk
1 tablespoon butter or margarine
1 teaspoon vanilla extract

Combine cocoa and sugar in a small saucepan; stir in milk. Cook over low heat, stirring constantly, just until mixture comes to a boil. Remove from heat; add butter and vanilla, stirring until butter melts. Serve warm over ice cream. Store in refrigerator.

QUICK HOT FUDGE SAUCE

1 cup sugar
⅓ cup cocoa
2 tablespoons all-purpose flour
¼ teaspoon salt
1 tablespoon butter or margarine
1 cup boiling water
1 teaspoon vanilla extract

Combine first 5 ingredients in a saucepan, stirring well. Gradually add water; cook over medium heat, stirring constantly, until smooth and thickened. Bring to a boil; boil 2 minutes. Stir in vanilla. Serve hot over cake or ice cream. Store in refrigerator. Yield: 1¼ cups.

HOT FUDGE SAUCE

4 (1-ounce) squares unsweetened chocolate
2 tablespoons butter or margarine
¾ cup boiling water
2 cups sugar
3 tablespoons light corn syrup
2 teaspoons vanilla extract

Combine chocolate, butter, and water in a heavy saucepan; cook over low heat until chocolate melts, stirring constantly. Add sugar and corn syrup, stirring well. Bring mixture to a boil; reduce heat, and simmer, uncovered, 7 minutes without stirring. Remove from heat, and stir in vanilla.

Serve warm over ice cream. Store in refrigerator. Yield: 2⅓ cups.

CINNAMON-FUDGE SAUCE

2 (1-ounce) squares unsweetened chocolate
1 tablespoon butter or margarine
⅓ cup boiling water
1 cup sugar
¼ teaspoon ground cinnamon
1 tablespoon corn syrup
1 teaspoon vanilla extract

Combine chocolate, butter, and water in a heavy saucepan; cook over low heat until chocolate melts, stirring constantly. Add sugar, cinnamon, and corn syrup, stirring well. Bring mixture to a boil; reduce heat, and simmer 7 minutes without stirring. Remove from heat, and stir in vanilla. Cool. Serve over cake or ice cream. Store in refrigerator. Yield: 1¼ cups.

CHOCOLATE-ORANGE SAUCE

½ cup whipping cream
1 (4-ounce) package sweet baking chocolate
½ teaspoon orange extract
¼ teaspoon grated orange rind

Place whipping cream in a heavy saucepan. Cook over low heat just until thoroughly heated (do not boil). Remove from heat. Add chocolate; stir until melted. Stir in orange extract and orange rind. Chill. Serve over ice cream. Store in refrigerator. Yield: ¾ cup.

OLD-FASHIONED CHOCOLATE SAUCE

1 cup sugar
¼ cup plus 1 tablespoon cocoa
3 tablespoons all-purpose flour
1 cup milk
2 tablespoons butter or margarine
1 teaspoon vanilla extract

Combine first 4 ingredients in a medium saucepan. Cook over medium heat, stirring constantly, until slightly thickened. Remove from heat, and stir in butter and vanilla. Serve warm over ice cream. Store in refrigerator. Yield: 2 cups.

HEAVENLY CHOCOLATE SAUCE

½ cup butter or margarine
4 (1-ounce) squares unsweetened chocolate
3 cups sugar
1 (12-ounce) can evaporated milk
½ teaspoon salt

Place butter and chocolate in top of a double boiler; bring water to a boil. Reduce heat to low; cook until chocolate melts. Stir in sugar, milk, and salt. Cook over medium heat, stirring constantly, until smooth. Serve warm over ice cream. Store in refrigerator. Yield: about 4 cups.

CHOCOLATE-PEANUT BUTTER SAUCE

1 (6-ounce) package semisweet chocolate morsels
¼ cup crunchy peanut butter
¼ cup light corn syrup
¼ cup plus 1 tablespoon whipping cream

Place chocolate morsels in top of a double boiler; bring water to a boil. Reduce heat to low; cook until chocolate melts. Add peanut butter, stirring until blended. Remove from heat, and stir in corn syrup and whipping cream. Serve warm over ice cream. Store in refrigerator. Yield: about 1¼ cups.

KAHLÚA-CHOCOLATE SAUCE

6 (1-ounce) squares semisweet chocolate
½ cup Kahlúa or other coffee-flavored liqueur
1 tablespoon powdered sugar

Place chocolate in top of a double boiler; bring water to a boil. Reduce heat to low; cook until chocolate melts. Remove from heat; gradually stir in Kahlúa and sugar, stirring until smooth. Cool; serve with fresh fruit or ice cream. Store in refrigerator. Yield: ¾ cup.

CHOCOLATE FONDUE SAUCE

1 (12-ounce) package semisweet chocolate morsels
½ cup half-and-half
½ cup sugar
1 teaspoon vanilla extract

Combine all ingredients in top of a double boiler; bring water to a boil. Reduce heat to low; cook until chocolate melts. Pour into fondue pot; place over fondue burner. Serve with fruit or cookies as dippers. Store in refrigerator. Yield: 2 cups.

CHOCOLATE FROSTING

2¼ to 2¾ cups sifted powdered sugar
¼ cup plus 1 tablespoon cocoa
¼ cup butter or margarine, melted
2 tablespoons milk
1 teaspoon vanilla extract
⅛ teaspoon salt

Combine 2¼ cups powdered sugar and remaining ingredients; beat at medium speed until thick enough to spread, adding additional sugar as needed to make a good spreading consistency. Yield: enough for one 1-layer cake.

QUICK FUDGE FROSTING

1 cup firmly packed brown sugar
3 tablespoons cocoa
3 tablespoons shortening
1 tablespoon butter or margarine
¼ teaspoon salt
⅓ cup milk
1½ cups sifted powdered sugar
1 teaspoon vanilla extract

Combine first 6 ingredients in a saucepan. Cook over medium heat, stirring constantly, until mixture boils; boil 3 minutes, stirring constantly. Remove from heat; cool.

Add powdered sugar and vanilla; beat at medium speed of an electric mixer until smooth and thick enough to spread, adding a small amount of milk, if necessary. Spread immediately on cooled cake. Yield: enough for one 2-layer cake.

CREAMY CHOCOLATE FROSTING

¼ cup butter or margarine
2 (1-ounce) squares unsweetened chocolate
2 cups sifted powdered sugar
⅓ cup evaporated milk
Pinch of salt
¼ teaspoon vanilla extract

Place butter and chocolate in top of a double boiler; bring water to a boil. Reduce heat to low; cook until chocolate melts. Add sugar, milk, and salt; beat at medium speed of an electric mixer until smooth and thick enough to spread. Stir in vanilla. Yield: enough for one 2-layer cake.

HONEY-CHOCOLATE FROSTING

3 tablespoons butter or margarine, softened
3 tablespoons cocoa
¾ teaspoon vanilla extract
1 cup sifted powdered sugar
1 tablespoon milk
1 tablespoon honey

Cream butter; add cocoa, beating well at low speed of an electric mixer. Add vanilla, sugar, milk, and honey; beat until smooth and thick enough to spread. Yield: enough for one 1-layer cake.

PROCESSOR CHOCOLATE FROSTING

½ cup butter or margarine, softened
4 cups sifted powdered sugar
¾ cup cocoa
½ cup evaporated milk
1 teaspoon Grand Marnier or other orange-flavored liqueur

Position knife blade in food processor bowl; add all ingredients in order listed. Top with cover; pulse 2 or 3 times. Process about 1 minute, scraping sides of processor bowl occasionally until smooth and thick enough to spread. Yield: enough for one 2-layer cake.

CHOCOLATE-ALMOND FROSTING

½ cup semisweet chocolate morsels
¼ cup milk
¼ cup plus 2 tablespoons butter
¼ to ½ teaspoon almond extract
1¼ cups sifted powdered sugar

Combine chocolate morsels, milk, and butter in a saucepan; cook over medium heat, stirring until chocolate melts. Remove from heat; add almond extract and powdered sugar, stirring well.

Set saucepan in ice; beat until frosting holds its shape and loses its gloss. If necessary, add a small amount of milk to make thick enough to spread. Yield: enough for 1 dozen cupcakes or one 1-layer cake.

CHOCOLATE FUDGE FROSTING

¼ cup butter or margarine, softened
⅓ cup light corn syrup
½ teaspoon vanilla extract
¼ teaspoon salt
½ cup cocoa
1 (16-ounce) package powdered sugar, sifted
2 to 3 tablespoons milk

Cream butter; add syrup, vanilla, salt, and cocoa, beating at medium speed of an electric mixer. Add sugar and milk alternately, beating until smooth and thick enough to spread. Yield: enough for one 2-layer cake.

CHOCOLATE GLAZE

2 tablespoons butter or margarine
1 (1-ounce) square unsweetened chocolate
1 cup sifted powdered sugar
2 tablespoons boiling water

Combine butter and chocolate in top of a double boiler; bring water to a boil. Reduce heat to low; cook until chocolate melts. Cool slightly. Add sugar and water; beat at low speed of an electric mixer until smooth enough to spoon over cake. Yield: enough for one tube or bundt cake.

Index

D

VICTORY OVER VERBAL ABUSE

A Healing Guide to Renewing Your Spirit and Reclaiming Your Life

Includes *Inspiring Affirmations* for Every Week of the Year

Patricia Evans

BESTSELLING AUTHOR OF *THE VERBALLY ABUSIVE RELATIONSHIP*

Avon, Massachusetts

Published by
Adams Media, a division of F+W Media, Inc.
57 Littlefield Street, Avon, MA 02322. U.S.A.
www.adamsmedia.com

ISBN 10: 1-4405-2580-3
ISBN 13: 978-1-4405-2580-3
eISBN 10: 1-4405-2773-3
eISBN 13: 978-1-4405-2773-9

Printed in the United States of America.

10 9 8 7 6 5 4

Library of Congress Cataloging-in-Publication Data
is available from the publisher.

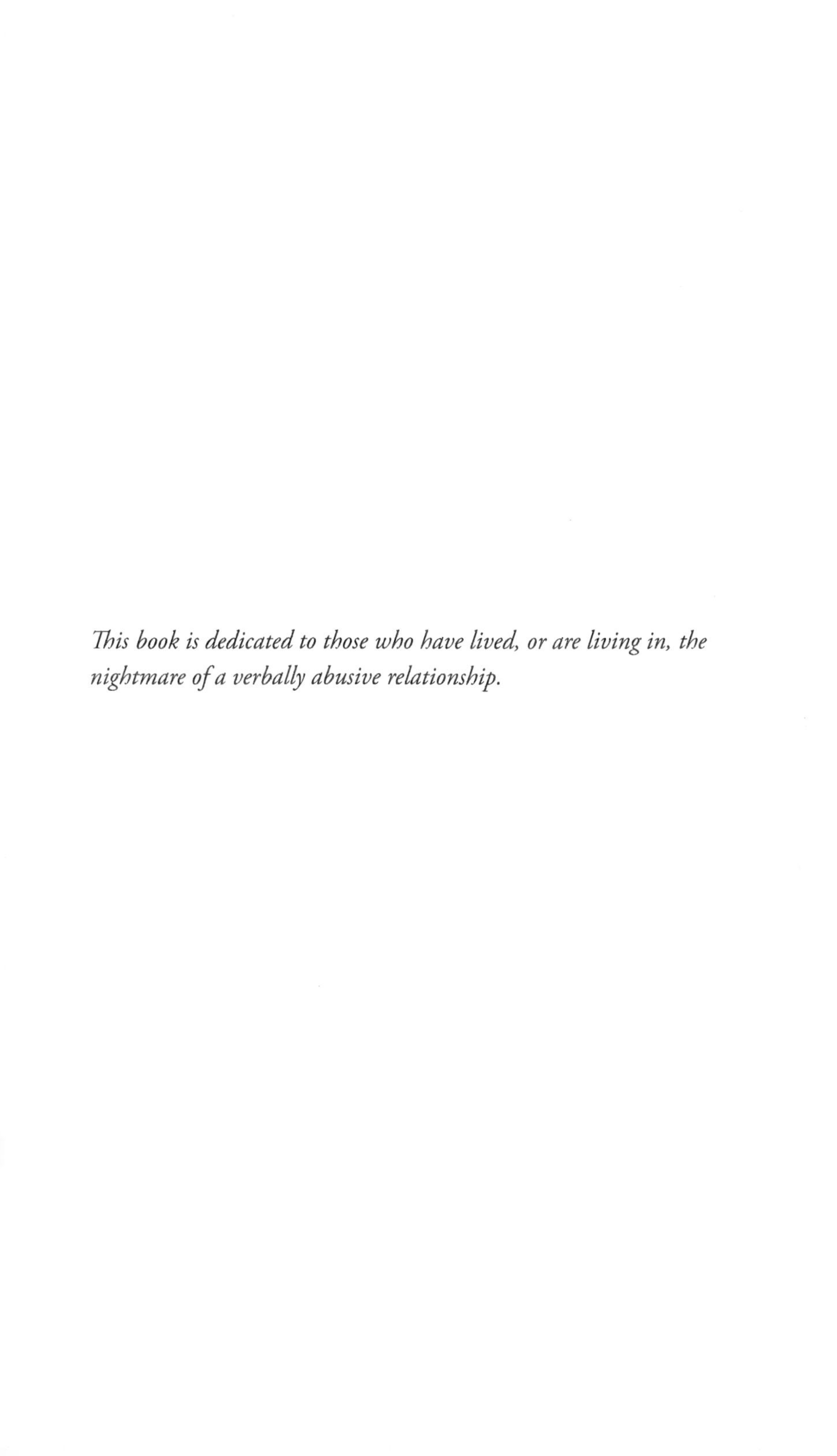

This book is dedicated to those who have lived, or are living in, the nightmare of a verbally abusive relationship.

Acknowledgments

I am deeply grateful to the thousands of people who have shared their lives with me. I have heard their strength and fragility, their clarity and confusion, their confidence and their self-doubt. I have learned from them. Thank you.

My patient and brilliant editor, Jennifer Lawler, has polished this book to shine for you. And my publishing mentor, Paula Munier, has been a patient guide on this journey. A special thanks to Catherine Young, MFT, CHT, and Sinead Flanagan, PhD, for their contributions.

Especially, I thank my family who have assisted me in many ways, including newsletter updates, editing inspiration, workshop programs, and office organization, but most of all I thank them for being there with their loving support.

Contents

Introduction

What Victory over Verbal Abuse Means

Victory over Verbal Abuse has been written to provide answers to many questions about verbal abuse and in particular to support recovery from the impact of verbal abuse. To recover from verbal abuse, it is essential to know that healing is possible. This book is designed to assist you on your journey to recovery, clarity, and personal power.

Abuse can begin anytime—in infancy, or in an adult relationship. It can be perpetrated by anyone who cannot tolerate your separateness and so attempts to shape you into his or her projected self, while ignoring your real self.

Thousands of cases testify to the fact that while some perpetrators have consciously malevolent motives, many, even most (especially in personal relationships), are responding to inner agonies generated in their own childhoods. Seemingly, because of their illusions, these agonizing moments are happening to them all over again, or so they experience the relationship. Thus, they can become extremely toxic to their partners, even without yelling or physically assaulting anyone. They can be so psychologically dangerous to the person or persons they target that they can eventually destroy the others' perceptions so as to leave them debilitated, physically ill, even suicidal. Personal victory over verbal abuse can best be equated with healing that brings clarity and peace to body, mind, and soul.

If you have experienced verbal abuse, you must know clearly that you are not responsible for anyone's abuse of you. You cannot make it happen to you. You may not be able to tell when it is happening to you. In a relationship, you know that the perpetrator is a separate person, but as strange as it seems, the perpetrator does not recognize you as a separate person. The perpetrator defines your inner world as if he or she were living within you.

Your victory also means clarity about who you are, what you like, what brings you satisfaction, along with awareness of your talents and gifts. Your victory is the journey you take to create what you want in your life—a life that gives you meaning and purpose and is most fulfilling. Your victory is fully realized when any fears, self-doubts, and confusing perceptions disappear.

As we collectively come to understand just what verbal abuse is and how it impacts humanity, we will have a healthier world. In this regard, victory over verbal abuse is extremely important to all who want to live in a world without war in any form—that is, people seeking power over other people. Achieving this can be one of our most important goals if we want to make it so. If we progress in achieving this victory, the dark cloud of verbal abuse will gradually dissipate in the light of awareness, just as the sun dispels the fog. This will make a difference in the lives of millions of people. For example, a dictator using verbally abusive and controlling behavior could not rise to power if most who witnessed verbal abuse recognized it for what it is!

People who are verbally abusive use Just Plain Senseless (JPS) negative statements that denigrate, accuse, imply, disparage, or in any other way define a person. They perpetrate defining behavior without examples, evidence, or facts. Verbal abuse is a lie told to you, about you, or about someone else. *It is most insidious when the accusations are perpetrated through implication.*

Here is an example of how insidious and evil implication can be. Jill is home with three children under six years of age. The twin girls are two years old. The oldest, a boy, is five. She is exhausted by the time her husband gets home from work, but she makes sure dinner is ready. Her husband Jack walks in, looks around, and sees a toy on the kitchen floor. He looks at the toy and says, "Look at this! *I* worked all day. It must be nice to have time for a nap."

Jill is shocked. She tries to defend herself against the implication that she doesn't work. "I don't have time for naps. I was taking care of the kids, the house, the meals, the laundry, and grocery shopping," she says evenly.

Jack sighs and rolls his eyes, picks up his five-year-old son, "Wanna go get a burger where the fun people are?" he asks his son.

"But dinner is ready," Jill says.

"We don't mind missing it, do we Jackie?" Little Jackie agrees, nodding at Jack who is so important in his life.

"Okay, my little man," says Jack.

He sets Jackie down, takes his hand, and heads out the door saying, "If anything's left, save it. I might want a midnight snack."

In personal relationships, some controllers disparage their partner in front of their children and so attempt to bond together with the children against the partner. This is very common. It's a way to gain power and feel connected; in some cases, it's the only way a controller feels connected to anyone. In the example above, Jack may have felt anger that the house didn't look as perfect as he desired. He may have resented that his wife didn't meet his expectations, which might have been to be admiring, maybe even adoring of him, when he arrived home.

When Jill told him what she had been doing all day, he shut her out completely, avoided recognizing her as a separate person, and subtly bonded with his son, Jackie, against her.

During the interaction, Jackie saw his dad ignore his mother, saw his dad sigh as if he had had all he could take, realized that mom was not much fun and that his dad approved of him, his "little man."

When he is an adult, Jackie may perpetrate the same behavior in his own relationships.

What could Jill have done? The best response to JPS behavior, even the most subtle, is to say something like, "Would you repeat that?" while holding up a video camera. Then, if he does repeat it, laugh and say, "That's what I thought you said." If he doesn't repeat it, he may be a bit more *conscious* that his behavior is senseless. This is a victory for consciousness. Victory over verbal abuse is victory for consciousness, while verbal abuse seeks its destruction.

How to Use This Book

Victory over Verbal Abuse is divided into two main parts. Part 1 is composed of chapters addressing different aspects of verbal abuse recovery. Part 2 contains weekly affirmations followed by a message that clarifies and reinforces the affirmation.

Millions of people suffer from verbal abuse from parents, partners, peers, and even cultures that define them. Thousands of women and some men have told me how they have suffered for years from what they have been told about themselves by others. Readers who contact me for information, consultations, and resources want to know how to recover from verbal abuse. Their questions and desire to recover compel me to respond.

The impact of verbal abuse is immeasurable. The shock and trauma are often disabling. A man told me this very morning, "The beatings ended when I was ten. I have forgotten them, but I cannot forget the verbal abuse." And women cry out, "I can't get the cruel things he said out of my thoughts." "I just don't know how to keep going and not keep hearing his words in my mind." Readers say, in so many words, "You gave me back my mind. I know I'm not crazy. Now I know there is a name for what I suffered, and I know what is wrong with abusers, *but how can I heal?*" *Victory over Verbal Abuse* presents a path to recovery.

Whether you have been put down or defined in any way, whether in childhood or as an adult, by anyone—a parent, sibling, teacher, school bully, coach, church leader, relative, or significant other—this book is written and designed to facilitate your recovery toward a lifetime of clarity and growth in awareness. Your victory over verbal abuse is our victory over the cloud of confusion that shadows our planet.

If someone has defined your inner world, told you what you are, what you think, feel, want, and so forth, you have heard verbal abuse. If you have been told, for example, "You're too sensitive," "You don't know what you're talking about," or "You can't do anything right," you have heard verbal abuse. Even if you have not been so defined, but instead been totally ignored, have not received a response to any question or comment, were defined as nonexistent, you, too, have been verbally abused. I believe this book will support you in building your confidence and self-esteem. Recovery *is* possible, whether you have suffered from verbal abuse in one or in many relationships.

Throughout these pages, most examples refer to women's experiences of verbal abuse because thousands of women have shared their stories with me. Nonetheless, the healing processes and affirmations should be of great support to men as well as to women.

Most of these men were told they were not good enough, would never amount to anything, and needed to toughen up. All the while, the emotional pain and mental anguish they suffered was not allowed expression by their abusers.

The information, resources, and affirmations are all meant to be your personal guide and are designed to support anyone who has suffered the confusion and betrayal of verbal abuse.

Questions about Healing from Verbal Abuse

- How do I ever trust again?
- How do I not feel so alone?
- How can I stop questioning myself, "Am I doing anything wrong?"
- How do I overcome my sadness and depression?
- How do I stop worrying?
- How do I relax?
- How do I get back my confidence and self-esteem?
- How can I know who I am and what I want to do now?
- How can I overcome my fear of being alone?
- How can I overcome my fear of ending up homeless?
- How can I recover the person I used to be?
- How can I sleep through the night?
- How can I stop the nightmares?
- How can I get past this exhaustion?
- How can I get those words out of my mind?
- How can I stop startling at every unexpected sound?
- How can I heal from trauma?
- How can I become the person I was meant to be?
- I know I am free to be me, but who am I?

Moving Forward

The following chapters light a path out of the cloud of verbal abuse, dissipating its blinding darkness. Beyond that, they offer insights and methods that support anyone striving to grow beyond where they are now.

No matter where you are on your own path of self-actualization, I believe you will feel stronger, clearer, more self-aware, and more determined much sooner than you might have thought possible by following every avenue this book opens up for you. Even if you thought you would never heal, much less be really happy, I am confident that, as you put the healing practices and affirmations into your daily routine, you will surprise yourself with the true self you discover.

I have heard from thousands of people who have described the steps they took to find peace, purpose, and passion, even beyond their highest expectations. I synthesize their journey for you. If you haven't already, I recommend that you find time to read my earlier four books that explain verbal abuse and control. Each gives you some information that facilitates healing.

The first, *The Verbally Abusive Relationship*, validates your experience of any relationship where you were defined.

The second, *Verbal Abuse Survivors Speak Out*, shows you some other forms of control that could have impaired your ability to be both self-defining and self-determined.

The third, *Controlling People*, shows what is "wrong with" the abuser, so any thought of blaming yourself is dissolved in new awareness.

The fourth, *The Verbally Abusive Man Can He Change?* shows how to wake up an abuser, if possible, and what it would take for an abuser to change.

These books help readers to see how irrational abusive behavior is and why, in relationships, abusers are usually much kinder to friends and neighbors than they are to their own partners.

It is my intention that, if you are recovering from anyone's attempt to control you and from the emotional pain and mental anguish of verbal abuse, whether overt or covert, perpetrated by anyone, in any circumstance, you will find strength and peace using this book to support you. It is meant to give you the determination to overcome any adversity. It is a guide to living your life with ever-increasing clarity, confidence, and caring—caring for yourself as much as you have cared for others. It can support you in setting your own goals and in achieving them.

Part 1

Recovery from Verbal Abuse

This section includes chapters that validate your experience of verbal abuse and address what verbal abuse looks like, how you can identify it, and what you can do to heal from it. This part explores how verbal abuse obscures clarity and limits your potential, how to recover when you are forced to remain in contact with a verbal abuser (such as when you have children together), and how to maintain a positive approach to recovery (even when it is difficult). The chapters in this part cover self-help processes to facilitate recovery, including how to discover and recover your greatest gifts and how to develop a strong sense of self. This part also includes a review of therapies to recover from trauma and shows you the steps to achieving victory over verbal abuse.

1

Validation

Being blamed, defined, and deprived can impact anyone's confidence, expectations, and aspirations. It can happen to anyone in the presence of *a person who indulges in verbal abuse* on a regular basis—henceforth referred to as the "abuser." In a world, or a relationship, that defines you, the process of recovery becomes a process of self-discovery. It is important to have hope and faith in yourself and to know that healing is possible. There is no room for despair, for giving up on yourself and your right to a peaceful, motivated, and happy life.

Control Through Verbal Abuse

Even if you have not been negatively defined in your personal life and relationships, you may have been defined by the dominant culture in which you live. One example is women defined as not as deserving of equal pay for equal work. Another is women defined as objects to be fought over by rival suitors. Another is men defined as not really men if they express their humanity in sadness, grief, and kindness to others; that is, if they are "toughened up" to be unfeeling and un-empathetic.

If you have been defined by anyone, especially if by a parent or spouse, please begin this journey knowing that you are not what you've been told and you are not alone. Additionally, you do not deserve any negative behavior or attitude, from the silent treatment to subtle implications, interrogations, accusations, threats, name-calling, or any other abuse.

Verbal abuse is an attempt to control you. When Mickey Rooney, claiming elder abuse, testified in court, he described how he was defined by those who would attempt to control him. In his testimony he was, in effect, speaking of his experience of verbal abuse. He revealed his experience in the advance testimony.

The testimony read:

> *Over the course of time, my daily life became unbearable. . . . I felt trapped, scared, used and frustrated. But above all, I felt helpless. . . . For years I suffered silently, unable to muster the courage to seek the help I knew I needed.*
>
> *Sometimes the transition from being in control of your life to having absolutely no control is swift, but other times it is so gradual that you wonder exactly when it truly began. In my case, I was eventually and completely stripped of the ability to make even the most basic decisions in my own life.*
>
> *You have the right to control your own life, to be happy, and not live in fear. Please, for yourself, end the cycle of abuse. Tell your story to anyone who will listen and above all, have hope.*

Those targeted by verbal abuse can become confused, adapted to the abuse, and brainwashed while their spirit and sense of self are eroded. This can happen to anyone who is under, or has been under, the influence of a person who, over time, defines them in a negative way. Part of healing is understanding how this could happen. Partners of abusers ask, "How I could have been so brainwashed that I thought there was something wrong with me?"

In some cases, the partner of an abuser may eventually come to the conclusion that something is wrong in the relationship but not know what it is. This is most common if the abuser is covert. The abuser may quietly counter nearly every comment and enthusiasm the partner expresses. Among other subtle responses the abuser may roll his eyes like "you're crazy," not respond to any question unless it is with another question, argue against all of the partner's views (even ones he has expressed as his own view in the past), and disguise cutting remarks as jokes.

A woman described how she'd experienced years of verbal assaults, diminishment, and disparaging comments about her abilities, spontaneity, and positive approach to life's problems. Most were cloaked as "just a joke," a "helpful" criticism, or an "offhand remark" that she took "too seriously." Without her realizing it, her basic nature was slowly eroding.

After her marriage ended, she met an old college classmate who told her he remembered her as a confident, vibrant, and dynamic person. That was when she realized the degree to which she had lost herself, for she was no longer the confident person she'd been. She wasn't at all sure of herself. She had trouble making decisions and she had trouble putting forth her best qualities even in a job interview. She didn't want to sound like she was "bragging." However, the good news was that since she remembered how she'd been she knew what she wanted. She wanted to reclaim her *Self*. She was determined to take every step she could to become herself again.

Recovery Through Validation

The path of recovery really begins when a person discovers that there is a name for her or his experience and a reason they didn't realize what was happening to them. This is validation! If you are uncertain about a relationship, I refer you to *The Verbally Abusive Relationship*, 3rd Edition (Adams Media, Inc., 2010). It was written to allow readers to recognize this kind of relationship.

If you have been the target of verbal abuse in any relationship, it may take some time to get past the pain verbal abuse inflicts—the loss of what you thought your abuser was, and the feelings of betrayal and shock that this could happen to you. If you have been targeted by verbal abuse, you may not only experience assaults to your own identity, but also, believing that your abuser is somehow rational, you may become confused and feel that there must be something wrong with you. While in this kind of relationship if you try to reason with the abuser, you only become more confused. The more you try to explain that you are not what the abuser says, the more the abuser escalates the abuse.

You are not alone, even though friends or relatives of your abuser did not see the abuse, nor even believe your experience. You stand with the millions of people who have had the same experience. And many have discovered that most abusers don't abuse in front of other people.

As you come to see how no one can define your inner world and that verbal abuse is irrational and ridiculous, you are on the path to healing. The verbal abuser tells you what your motives, thoughts, and feelings are, as if he or she were you. How crazy is that! You are self-defining. You are not too sensitive, nor do you want to start a fight, nor are you any other negative comment you've been told about yourself. But even if you know that what an abuser says is nonsense, it is still a blow to your mind and consciousness.

Sometimes friends and family have no understanding of verbal abuse. When you try to explain your experience, you may hear something like, "He is so nice. I don't see how that could have happened."

Your response might be, "Oh, I understand how you feel. Even a murderer's in-laws said they didn't think he could have done anything to their daughter. He was so nice. That was until they found out he had killed her."

Maybe you have been so insidiously controlled you didn't know what was happening to you. I want to validate your experience right here. Following are some of the feelings people have had when they were in a relationship with a person who verbally abused them. If you recognize these feelings, your feelings are validating you.

You May Feel Brainwashed

Verbal abuse so wholly defines its target that it is like brainwashing. If you are, or have been the target of verbal abuse:

1. You may have been told that you are not who you have known yourself to be. For example, if you sought peace and a good relationship, you were told that you "want to argue," or that you "don't care." This kind of abuse breaks down your identity.
2. You may have begun to feel guilty, especially if you received constant criticism or correction that implied that you should do better, just don't measure up, aren't good enough, or aren't smart enough.
3. You may have begun to believe that the negative, demeaning, or critical comments the abuser made about you were true. In other words, you may have internalized the words,

accepting them as if they were true. This is so, especially, if your abuser offered some relief, that is, he acted as if nothing happened—as if you had nothing to complain about. And, conversely, if you commented on what he said, explaining that what he said wasn't true, he accelerated the abuse.

4. Eventually, if you were abused over time, you may have sought relief from your confusion, lost identity, and feelings of unworthiness by trying harder to please, to comply with the abuser and mainly *to adopt the abuser's view of you.* You may have come close to losing your Self.

You May Feel Betrayed

Verbal abuse lies to you. If the person who promised to love you and claimed to love you then proceeded to attempt to erase your mind, your awareness, your very consciousness by telling you what you are, think, feel, even your motives, or that what you just heard and saw didn't happen, your abuser has attempted to deceive you and so, of course, you may feel betrayed.

Further validation comes with knowing that verbal abuse is not only a lie told to you about you, it may also be a lie told to others about you. And conversely, a lie told to you about others.

I had not finished this paragraph when a woman called to tell me that she had attended a Sunday service at a church in a very small town in almost the exact middle of the United States. The members listened to the minister define the population of California not as what they are, but as "evil," and enjoined the congregation to pray with him that the entire state would fall into the ocean. They complied, except for the woman who called me after the service. Having lived away from this community, she saw the contrast between normal people and people who would have more than thirty-seven million be dead or be displaced.

The congregation listened to the minister, a wolf disguised as a shepherd, because his disguise fooled them. They were betrayed. They were lied to. The woman who called me knew the congregation was misled by the minister's persona of kindness, charity, and wisdom. She had believed in him herself until this incident. Similarly, the partners of abusers feel betrayed when they realize that the abuser, who first appeared so kind, is actually abusive and controlling. This switch from good to bad behavior is explained in *Controlling People* (Adams Media, Inc., 2002). Similarly, I talked with a woman who realized that the lies told to her about her family, were indeed, lies. Throughout her marriage her husband had consistently and subtly disparaged her parents and relatives. As time passed, his comments ridiculed and even made fun of them, and gradually he convinced her of his views. She became somewhat isolated from them. She had a general feeling that they were not very intelligent, sophisticated, or even well educated. As she began to recognize his verbal abuse of her, she started to think about her family and she realized that they were all high achievers and highly educated. Her grandfather had been a doctor and her mother had a professional career when not many women did and her cousin was well-known. "In a way," she said, "they're all the opposite of what he said. At last, I am proud of my family."

You May Feel That It's Somehow Your Fault—Abuse Internalized

Many women who have been in a verbally abusive relationship and who have also experienced physical abuse say that verbal abuse is worse. Of course there are exceptions, but in general, recovery from verbal abuse takes longer because verbal abuse is about the erasure of mind, and ultimately the destruction of consciousness.

People on the outside looking in on a verbally abusive relationship might wonder how verbal abuse can be so bad. One reason seems to be that when a person sees a blow coming or their life is threatened, they often disassociate from the terror. Later they don't remember much of what happened in those moments. Then they see the evidence, a bruise, and feel the pain, but their mind is not focused into what is happening second by second.

On the other hand, when people hear verbal abuse—orders, criticism, or angry outbursts—directed at them from someone they trust, are in a relationship with, or look up to, they may, over time, begin to believe what they are told. If they don't know that what they are hearing is actually verbal abuse, they may try harder to please their abuser. They may become depressed. They may spend years explaining themselves to the abuser. They may build their identity around what they're told. They may internalize the words they hear, thinking, for example, "I'm too sensitive," or, "I'm blowing things out of proportion," or "I can't do anything right."

Quite unlike battering, verbal abuse affects the partner's mind, impacting its organization and thought processes. When the partner hears something like, "You're too sensitive. You just want to argue," *she is totally focused into her mate's words,* trying to make sense of them, trying to figure out:

1. Why he thinks she wants to argue.
2. How she can get back to the issue that might have been something like, "I'm just saying that I didn't think that comment, that you said was 'just a joke,' was funny."
3. How to explain that she doesn't want to argue.

Failing to accomplish these efforts, she gives up. She is silenced. Furthermore, if the abuser is periodically *non*abusive, she cannot reconcile the two opposite experiences. Mental anguish, racing thoughts, and exhaustion can all ensue. Physical scars heal; however, the scars of verbal abuse linger for years. They have invaded her psyche.

You May Feel Afraid of Your Abuser

If you are with someone you fear because he is periodically out of control, threatens your life, hits, pushes, grabs or shoves you, blocks your escape, falsely imprisons you, demonstrates violence, harms or threatens to harm your child, don't try to get your abuser to see what he is doing, or explain to him what is bothering you. Instead, call your local domestic violence prevention program or the national domestic violence hotline for help, and then tell all.

Recovery takes time but once you are safe from contact with the abuser, I hope you will focus on your success and how strong you can be in your stand against abuse. You will have the knowledge to help others.

Following is a true account of a case that, while extreme, illustrates the power of words. A woman was forced to sit and listen to her well-liked and well-known spouse rage for hours. What hold did her husband have over her? What words bound her to her chair? "If you move, the kids will pay, and believe me, you don't want to know how." His abuse had escalated. She had been taught to be powerless. This man's inexplicable rage—a torrent of accusation and blame—was matched only by her fear and confusion. But now, because of the children, she knew he was crazy and that meant *she* wasn't. "With his power," she thought, "I know he will take everything, but I am willing to give away everything but I won't give away my soul."

Planning her escape with her children did take time. Records had to be built. How could she ever leave her children alone with a "crazy" man? Who would believe her? No bruises. No black eyes. Who wouldn't believe him, with a highly perfected and charming persona—the one he showed to the world? What could she do when he had his wealth and she didn't have a penny? Powerless as she felt, she began to ask for help and so her recovery began.

At times she was traumatized, but saw on a regular basis a supportive and knowledgeable therapist who was skilled in trauma therapy. There were times when she could remember little of what had just happened. She temporarily disassociated. And there was a time she was flooded with flashing memories of literally hundreds of shocking behaviors perpetrated by her now ex-husband. Even after her divorce, she was attacked and punched in the chest during a child exchange. Breathless, she did call the police, and this time they protected her. She built a team through trial and error. She never gave up. She now has the support of doctors, lawyers, and others who will see her through, freeing her children from his unsupervised visits with them—the ones where they are terrorized, just as she was.

Her children are getting therapy for trauma and its impact. And, like many of my readers, she will speak out, bringing awareness to others and saving lives. This, too, is part of recovery. This, too, fuels her determination.

An Awful Feeling—What Is It?

Many women who have been married to or in long-term relationships with abusive men have told me about being overcome by a feeling that seemed to immobilize them. It was an awful feeling that something terrible would befall them. It happened at different times. For example, they started to feel it if they talked to someone about a problem in their relationship. They felt it as a kind of guilty anxiety if they bought a book about it. They felt it a lot more if they opened their own safety deposit box with cash so their spouse wouldn't know. They felt it even if they wanted the safety deposit box only to store some personal, private records. They got the same feeling, even worse, if they opened a savings account in their own name to deposit cash gifts from their own family without telling their spouse about it. They felt like they needed to report to their spouse about what they were doing but, at the same time, they did not want to tell him. They didn't want to share this information with him because they didn't want to hear an interrogation about it, or anger about it, or some sarcastic put-down about it. Of course, talking to a lawyer just to gather information in case their relationship became intolerable was an intolerable thought.

Naming the Awful Feeling

These women were feeling dread. What is dread? It is a feeling that you will experience some unknown and unnamed doom if you proceed. People who experience dread feel a terror or overwhelming fear of what might happen if they do what they were thinking of doing, or if they actually do it despite feeling that something bad will happen to them.

But why would a person feel dread about saving some money, or securing private documents, or gathering information about a possible life change? The answer can be found in what these women all had in common. They were all acting, or about to act, on their own behalf without permission from a man.

The feeling of dread comes from a long history of oppression—social as well as personal. Women in particular have experienced many accusations, burnings at the stake, beheadings, and deaths by stoning in the past, and in some places, in the present. Consequently, our collective history or memory holds an authoritarian power tantamount to an earth-shattering voice descending from the skies, parting the clouds, and booming, "Thou shall not. . . ." Many women feel as if they are breaking a taboo to act on their own behalf without permission from a man.

An unwritten taboo that is still built into most cultures is about the subjugation of women.

The evil taboo: "You may not act without permission from a man."

The fear: "Acting on your own behalf will bring you harm."

Five Steps to Overcoming the Awful Feeling

If you have felt dread when acting on your own behalf without permission from a significant other, these steps may help you to overcome it.

First, know that the feeling of dread comes from breaking a taboo. Just knowing what this feeling is about and that it doesn't represent anything that will happen in your future helps to dissolve it.

Second, talk to yourself in a positive way. Here are some examples:

- "I am acting on my own."
- "I am opposing a bad, ridiculous, controlling, enslaving rule."
- "Acting on my own is a great, good thing. My guardian angel is applauding me, as are all the saints and angels."
- "The universe supports me because I am exercising my free will, bringing no harm to others, and doing something really good for me."

Third, look for support from people who are really there for you. Family, friends, and online support groups are all possibilities.

Fourth, notice that the feeling fades away and over time ceases to reappear.

Fifth, notice that no doom befalls you.

Coping with a Verbal Abuser

If you're the partner of an abuser, you need to arm yourself with the knowledge of just how delusional your abuser is. You can't give weight to the abusive words. You must constantly remind yourself that the negative, abusive statements are simply the lies that bullies indulge in—pretend talk—by someone who seeks to silence you, their target, so they can seemingly continue to pretend to be God, to know what you want, think, and are trying to do. Armed with this knowledge, you won't be in a fog, and you won't wonder if you are crazy. You won't keep trying to figure it out. You will see that you are hearing nonsense. You are looking at the abuser from an observer's standpoint.

After stating your request that your abuser not define you as if he knew your motives and thoughts, if he continues, you observe as a scientist and your mind isn't caught up in trying to make sense of nonsense. You know he is irrational and so you don't waste a moment of your time trying to explain to him how what he said wasn't true. You know you cannot reason with an irrational person. You don't react defensively. Instead, you respond with disbelief. Here are some suggestions:

- "What?"
- "What did you say?"
- "Did you just tell me what I am?"

- "Did you just tell me what I do? That is so silly. You are not me and do not know what I am, or what I am doing, or my motives."

You see he is impaired and severely compromised. What he says has a less destructive impact. And, now there is something you can do. You can see if you can wake him up to his nonsensical behavior and see if he is willing to get help. Or you can make a plan to leave.

If You Feel Powerless

When you feel that there is nothing that you can do, you may be deeply traumatized. One way to overcome the feeling of powerlessness is to know that there is something you *can* do. Plan not to react, but to respond. Verbal abuse is traumatizing; however, when you know that it is irrational nonsense and that there is something you can do, it may be less traumatizing. Try preparing yourself by asking yourself, "What can I do the next time I am defined?" If, for instance, you can respond with "nonsense" and walk away, you may be empowered to take other steps as well.

When considering the toxicity of verbal abuse, it's not the snake bite (the hostility of the attack). It's the venom! The venom is in the nonsensical statement. It can permeate your psyche if you try to make sense of it or explain to the abuser why it is wrong. The bite (the fact that the abuser attacked)fades like a bruise, but the venom can permeate your mind and soul.

When it comes to Jekyll and Hyde behavior—that is, an abuser's first being kind, then unkind—you don't need to try to figure out, "Is he a saint or a sinner, a devil or an angel?" You only need to know that he may be just plain toxic to you!

I invite you to think of anything negative you've been told about yourself that could shape your sense of self and ask yourself if you have come to think it's true or if you used to think it was in some way true. Has anyone told you that you are made wrong? That you are too sensitive? Has anyone entered your mind and told you that you are jumping to conclusions, or blowing things out of proportion? Has anyone told you that you do everything wrong? If so, you have heard irrational statements!

Over time, these assaults, and possibly hundreds of others, do have a serious impact. By understanding the deep impact of verbal abuse, you will be clearer about your healing and recovery, I believe. Although it can take time and determination to recover, the benefits are worth it—you will become a stronger, more confident, self-defining person, empowered from within to be self-defining and who you were really meant to be.

Most people feel compelled to discover and develop their gifts and talents and, ultimately, to make a positive difference in the lives of others. The process of "becoming" is lifelong. Isn't that what makes the journey exciting? The better you know yourself, the more successful you will be, not just financially, but in terms of satisfaction, a sense of accomplishment, and appreciation of yourself.

Recovery is all about dissolving the influence of negative comments and demeaning treatment as well as the underlying, and sometimes unrecognized, feelings of inadequacy, unworthiness, and low self-esteem that such treatment generates. And it is about discovering and using your gifts.

Your recovery is greatly facilitated by the knowledge that you don't say to the abuser what the abuser says to you; that what he says is a lie told to you, about you, and it is completely irrational.

Also know that if you even see the handwriting of a former abuser, you may feel unsure, stirred up inside, unable to feel the energy that you felt before. This is because you are re-traumatized. Just as a person who suffered trauma in a war might feel shattered upon hearing a firecracker unexpectedly go off, you will feel the same shock. Know that in a few days you will feel yourself again. If you do receive any money from him in, for instance, child support, try to have it transferred automatically to a bank account you set up for that purpose.

As you heal from the emotional pain, mental anguish, and physical impact of verbal abuse, you can lead an increasingly satisfying life. As a survivor, you have great potential whatever your age or circumstance. After all, you have survived the oppression of verbal abuse. Imagine what you can do when not subject to it.

Now let's look at the ways people have coped with verbal abuse and how to manage if you must be in contact with an abuser.

Guidelines: Separated but Still in Contact with the Abuser

Recovery from verbal abuse is difficult if you are in contact with your abuser because you are reminded of the past. Just seeing the abuser's name in an e-mail or on a check can re-traumatize you. However, in some cases circumstances require that you have some contact with your abuser. If this is your situation, you may hear verbal abuse again, even if the abuser is trying to reform. It takes time and extensive therapy for abusers to change.

Even if you have completely or temporarily separated from your relationship, you may have meetings or conversations with the person who abused you. If you are sharing custody, you may have to discuss child-related decisions. Any contact may re-traumatize you; however, if you are prepared to protect yourself you will feel more empowered and will be on the path to recovery.

- Tell the abuser that you will not accept the statements that define you and list examples.
- Tell your abuser that you will video all meetings. Then keep a video camera with you.
- Limit contact with the abuser.
- Say, "What did you say?" if you do hear verbal abuse.
- Be prepared to leave the presence of the abuser if you are abused.
- Hang up the phone if you are abused.
- Try to keep any necessary communication via e-mail, not phones or text messages.
- Save abusive e-mail as evidence but don't respond.
- Never text if you are bombarded with texts from your abuser.
- Never go where your safety is threatened.
- Trust your intuition.
- Don't explain or defend yourself.
- Don't try to lock your abuser out of a home he owns with you. Instead, leave or make a plan about where you will go. Call 911 if you are threatened with physical violence.
- A restraining order may be possible. Always get legal advice.
- If you are exchanging children, try to arrange a safe exchange at a neutral site.
- Don't hesitate to report physical abuse or threats to your life.
- Don't hesitate to call the National Domestic Violence Hotline for information and resources in your area. That number is 1–800–799–SAFE (7233).
- If you are separated or divorcing but living in the same house because of economic or other reasons, here are some suggestions. Use a note pad to leave important information. Divide the house as well as the cupboards and refrigerator. Each person is responsible for his or her own meals and laundry.

You have already come a long way toward recognizing verbal abuse and determining that you want it out of your life. The next chapter offers guidelines that are designed to assist you in removing not only negative people from your life but also the negative comments that may have been programmed into your mind. The goal is to gain increasing trust in yourself so that your confidence grows. No more second-guessing, "Did I say that right?" No more self-doubt, "Shouldn't I feel better by now?" "Will I ever feel like myself again?"

If you take one day at a time, as in all processes, I am confident that you, like thousands of women I have talked to, will continue to grow, to find essential meaning and purpose in your life, and to feel personal power that is your right.

2

Recovery from Verbal Abuse

To begin healing from verbal abuse, you may find it helpful to follow some general guidelines. These basic guidelines are suggestions that have benefited many. However, they are recommendations, not the Ten Commandments. In all things, my highest recommendation is that you allow your intuition to guide you and that you love yourself.

Guidelines for Recovering from Verbal Abuse

1. Stay away from people who define you. This is a goal that may take time to achieve. As you become more aware, you may realize that a friend is more a critic than a friend to you, or that a relative has been, and may always be, controlling toward you. You may need to pull away from some people and send a card rather than make a phone call, or meet on Facebook instead of a coffee shop, or block a toxic person from your Facebook page (and your life) altogether.

2. Monitor your thoughts. You are in charge of your thoughts. No one can stop you from monitoring your thoughts—that is, being mindful. If you are alert to any negative thoughts, such as, "If I were smarter, I wouldn't have been in this mess," change the thought to a positive one. For example, "I am smart and getting smarter all the time. Anyone can be fooled by an abuser and when the bad behavior shows up, an abuser can be very convincing that it is the partner's fault."
3. Don't blame yourself for not making the relationship work. Know that no one can fix an abuser. A verbal abuser is damaged and only the abuser can fix himself or herself with intensive therapy.
4. Don't blame yourself for choosing the relationship. Anyone can be fooled by an abuser because nearly all verbal abusers present perfectly to their partners in couple relationships until they feel secure, then they project their lost selves into their partners. I suggest that you read *Controlling People* if you would like to understand more about the "lost self" and how it can be projected into you and then often withdrawn when you leave.
5. Gather information. Learn everything you can about verbal abuse and controlling behavior so that you will recognize anyone's attempt to define you in any way. The more knowledge you have about verbal abuse, the safer and more empowered you will feel.
6. Find support. Tell only those you can trust what you are going through or have gone through. Don't expect everyone to understand. Many people don't. Join an online support group, a divorce support group, or a grief recovery group. One verbal-abuse support group can be found at *www.verbalabuse.com*.

7. Develop confidence and self-esteem. Stay focused on your goals. A positive attitude and even the smallest success can increase your self-esteem.
8. Don't look back. Remind yourself to stay in the present and plan for the future. The past is gone. If you think of the name of the abuser or something the abuser said, or something that happened with the abuser, say "erase!" and focus on the present and something nearby such as counting the buttons on the phone, or the total in your checkbook.
9. Prepare for dealing with your abuser. If circumstances require you to stay in contact with your abuser, see the guidelines in Chapter 1 for coping with this situation. Be aware that contact can re-traumatize you and take steps to prepare yourself.
10. Use this book to stay focused on your healing path. Never hesitate to make your path *your* own, to follow your intuition and to love yourself.

Verbal Abuse as Blame

If you trust and love a person and then hear him yelling at you, putting you down, giving you the silent treatment, countering your every thought, or accusing you, it can be very difficult not to think that you have inadvertently said or done something wrong, something that provoked the abuser. It can be extremely confusing if the abuser was very kind and seemed to be a different person at the beginning of the relationship. (My previous book, *Controlling People*, fully explains this switch.)

It is easy to believe that you have somehow provoked the abuser. It is easy to think that it is you who is somehow at fault. After all, that is what you're told. It is hard to realize that the abuse is not your fault.

For all these reasons and more, it is very important that anyone who has heard, "If you change, your abuser will change," understand that this is a blaming statement that implies that you are responsible for the abuser's behavior. You are not.

Taking Care of Yourself

The most important thing you can do right now to recover is to take care of yourself. Here are some tips for getting started:

1. Reduce stress and avoid people who verbally abuse you or denigrate others behind their backs.
2. Get some exercise daily.
3. Eat some live food—greens daily.
4. Love yourself by talking nicely to yourself.
5. Care for yourself like you would care for the sweetest, most innocent child you could ever imagine.
6. Go where you feel like you are yourself. If you feel good around people in a coffee shop, or alone by a lake, or even in your favorite department store, that is where to go when you feel down.
7. Know that what is communicated to us affects us but negative programming can be erased.
8. Deprivation impacts the psyche as well as words do, so by knowing what is normal one may realize the deprivation to be overcome.
9. Know the source and impact of verbal abuse; thus, you can become clear and what you've been told will lose its influence upon you.
10. Discover your own overriding goal.

11. Pursue your passion to always bring meaning to your life. Some examples are to be an artist, singer, songwriter, yoga practitioner, volunteer.
12. Life is about self-discovery and increasing awareness. Life is a journey.

Finding What's Healthy and Normal

A woman told me, "My supervisor, with whom I'd become friends, said, 'Do you realize that you've been abused for so long, you've forgotten what healthy, normal behavior is?'"

Look within at how you feel in the presence of others. If you feel comfortable, uplifted, encouraged, understood, you are experiencing healthy, normal behavior. Here are some attributes of healthy normal people. They:

- Don't define you and your inner world
- Ask you about you, rather than only talk about themselves
- Share themselves with you rather than remain secretive
- Are spontaneous, not compulsive
- Are calm, not angry
- Are conversational, not silent
- Are expressive, not stilted
- Express empathy and understanding, not anger
- Apologize if they make a mistake, not blame you

Healing from the Impact of Verbal Abuse

Knowing the impact of verbal abuse and knowing that the real you can emerge from the limitations that verbal abuse instills are essential. As a partner or child of an abuser, you may experience many different symptoms. If you find that you are experiencing some of these symptoms from recent or past abuse, please know that healing is possible. You are one of millions of people throughout the world who react to the blows of verbal abuse in similar ways. You are not alone. You are not crazy.

Symptoms Chart

Verbal Abuse Creates Emotional Pain	Verbal Abuse Creates Mental Anguish
Sadness	Confusion
Difficulty remembering what happened	Feeling a setback after feeling fine
Anxiety	Panic
Low self-esteem	Grief
Guilt	Hopelessness
Racing thoughts	Worrying
Sleeplessness	Nightmares
Crying spells	Inability to focus on one thing for long
Feeling scattered	Feeling stirred up inside
Feeling irritable	Depression
Anger	Fear of the future or of more abuse
Loneliness	Hypervigilance
Embarrassment	Betrayal
Shame	Shock

Physical and Behavioral Symptoms of Verbal Abuse

Physical Symptoms	Behavioral Symptoms
Weight loss or gain	Isolating self from others
Insomnia and fatigue	Compulsive behaviors
Exhaustion	Inability to make decisions
Muscle pain, backaches	Self-medication with drugs or alcohol
Stomach/digestive problems	Self-mutilation
Stress-related illnesses	Eating disorders
Immune system problems	

Recognizing What Doesn't Work and Why

Part of recovery depends on seeing clearly how difficult it is for those who are abused to understand what is happening and why. They try everything they can think of to improve their relationship and to protect their children, and they blame themselves when nothing works. They often say, "Before I understood what it was, I tried and tried to figure out what was wrong. And, I tried every way possible to get through to him. He seemed to get along with everyone but me. I couldn't figure it out." Following are some examples of what doesn't work that may validate your experience. If you are familiar with them, you already know they don't work with a confirmed verbal abuser.

Trying to Tell the Abuser How You Feel

If you are wondering why, when you tried to tell an abuser how you felt, nothing changed, it is because the abuser could not really hear you. If you find yourself going over conversations and trying to figure out why the abuser didn't really understand how you felt, it is because he couldn't. You are not alone in trying to explain your feelings. Usually one of the first things the partner of an abuser does when she is defined is tell the abuser how she feels. (The longest a woman I've talked to tried this was sixty-four years.)

If you try it once or twice—"I felt hurt when you said that"—and it doesn't elicit an apology, there is no evidence that it ever will work. If you start to think about an incident and what you could have, or should have said, focus on something else. Make it your goal to never tell a confirmed abuser how you feel. It doesn't work. Do make it a goal to say something like "nonsense" if you hear someone define you in the future.

Trying to Explain What Really Happened or What You Meant

Believing the abuser is rational, you may protest and try to explain to the abuser that what you are being told is not true. If, after being accused of something, you try to stop the abuse by explaining yourself to the abuser, you may be told that you are "trying to start a fight," "want to argue," or just as mind-boggling, "That's not the point." This declaration draws you in with a reasonable question, "Well, what is the point?" and the conversation becomes even more mind-boggling when the abuser replies, "You just don't get it."

Here is another version of "that's not the point." In this case, a man was being verbally abused by his wife. He heard the accusation, "You have to have everything your way." He asked, "What do you mean?"

"Well," his abusive wife said, "I have to put the car in the garage because you want it in the garage."

"What do you mean?" the husband asked. "I've never said I want you to put the car in the garage."

His wife responded, "That's not the point!"

"Well, what is the point?" he asked with great patience.

"If you don't get it, there is no point in my explaining it to you!"

Mind-boggling? Yes! Partners are not trying to start a fight, nor are they "not getting it" as if there is some yet-to-be-discovered flaw within them that they must "get" to repair the relationship. Unless people understand what verbal abuse is, they may be accused and abused, then blamed, even for their explanations. They may succumb to desperate confusion. Abusers do not hear explanations. They see them as attacks and fight back.

Verbally abusive statements are hostile. They attempt to define the actions and motives of anyone who tries to explain herself to an abuser, only increasing the trauma. When partners of abusers attempt to explain themselves to an abuser, they are assuming that their abuser is rational. Even domestic violence is often described as a couple "having a fight," or "a domestic dispute," as if two people entered a ring to fight, rather than that an attack is taking place. Over time, victims discover that explaining doesn't work with a confirmed abuser.

Trying Harder

Rather than explaining to the abuser that what was said isn't true, you may instead try to be invisible and compliant to avoid being targeted again. You try harder. Since negative definitions include so much blame, the partners of verbal abusers often try to fix themselves. Some go to therapists for years.

As you try to do better, be better, and do more, you may reach a state of complete exhaustion. The abuser brushes your efforts and feelings aside and you are blamed for the abuser's anger, irritable outbursts, or silent treatment. Your recovery requires that you discover that the abuse has nothing to do with you. The abuser has a problem.

Ignoring the Abuse

You may try telling yourself that you shouldn't let what you hear bother you. You may become numb and lose your sense of self, even becoming ill from the constant stress. You can no longer adapt, no longer reconstitute yourself. You discover that no matter how hard you try to ignore it, the abuse still hurts you. Blows to consciousness are like blows to your body. They take a toll.

Abusing Back

Some people who are subject to verbal abuse, especially the overt kind like name-calling, may try to abuse back, as if to say, "You call me a name, I'll call you a worse one, or maybe beat you up." This only subjects them to escalation, greater confusion, and feelings of guilt and, of course, more blame. Abusing back doesn't work. Healing comes with the realization that abusing back solves nothing. Sometimes a video camera does.

Believing Nonsense

Some partners and former partners of abusers hold family, cultural, or religious beliefs that trap them. Recognizing these beliefs, and realizing that they are only beliefs, not truths, supports their recovery.

You may believe:

- It takes two, so it's half your fault that you are abused.
- If you are nice to your mate, your mate will be nice to you.

- If you tell the abuser how you feel, the abuser will stop.
- A man is superior so what he says must be true.
- A woman may not act on her own behalf without permission from a man.
- A woman must submit to a man in marriage.

What Holds the Possibility of Working?

Now that we've talked about what doesn't work, let's look at some strategies that can work in a relationship with a verbal abuser.

Awareness

If you are in a verbally abusive relationship, I suggest that you try bringing awareness to the perpetrator by learning all you can about verbal abuse and what is wrong with the perpetrator. Then present him with a list of verbally abusive sentences and behaviors, using only ones that you have experienced. Four hundred samples of abusive sentences are listed in the appendix of *The Verbally Abusive Man Can He Change?*, as well as a list of behaviors for your reference. It may be necessary that you tell him that he must make every effort to stop if he is to have any relationship with you. If he won't work to change and you can't leave, try ignoring him until you can. Then, if he doesn't agree to do the work necessary to change, and you decide to leave, you can clearly state, "This is why I left you," followed by the list of his verbally abusive behaviors. If he does begin the work to change, it may be helpful to separate, with only planned meetings, until he completes the intensive therapy and work that hold the possibility of effecting change. If he is physically violent or your intuition tells you he may be dangerous in any way, you can e-mail him the list from a safe place.

In keeping with the goal of bringing awareness, here is a young man's unique approach. Although he considered other options, he finally chose the most effective—he called me for help. He told me that he was fifteen and he intended to spend his summer working out, every minute he could, so he would be stronger than anyone in his school and would learn to feel *nothing*. He wouldn't waste time explaining to the school bullies that what they said was not okay. Instead, he said that he would feel nothing so he wouldn't get hurt, and he would be so strong he could hurt them if they tried to hurt him. As we talked, he seemed to hear himself and suddenly said, "This might not be a good idea." I agreed. He said that he would figure out a better way to deal with the abusive kids at his school.

When school started again, he contacted me and sent me a PowerPoint presentation about verbal abuse—all about what he'd learned from my books. He had presented it to his class. He said they were speechless. The bullies in the room realized how irrational they'd been. Life at school improved. The bullies realized that everyone knew their name-calling was irrational and that their behavior was a sign of their weakness, not his. This is the empowering knowledge that supports all survivors' recovery.

Useful Tips

Here are some useful tips to support recovery from verbal abuse:

1. Keep people who indulge in verbal abuse out of your life as much as you possibly can.
2. Wake up the abuser, if possible, or leave.
3. Be with the abuser only if there is real change. That means he has done intensive psychotherapy, and you see that this

change has lasted over time. Many abusive men call me for a consultation as they do not know everything they would have to do to change, nor even what is wrong with them.

4. Have a plan to save yourself and any children you have.
5. Know that what you have been told about yourself is not true.
6. Know that you can recover, become self-defining, and be absolutely clear about who you are, your interests, needs, goals, and aspirations.
7. Affirm yourself and act on your own behalf every day.
8. Get all the support you can.
9. Change negative thoughts to positive ones.

Some Reminders

Since you do not make a person indulge in verbal abuse nor make a person stop indulging in verbal abuse, it is important that you begin the process of healing and recovery by reminding yourself of the following:

1. The assault of verbal abuse can last much longer and do more harm than being hit. It is your right, even your duty, to save yourself.
2. Something is wrong with the abuser. The abuse has nothing to do with you. It is simply directed at you like a drive-by shooting. The abuser doesn't see and hear the real you.
3. It is up to you to be as proactive as you can to use the support and resources available to you.
4. Honor the process. It takes time to heal.

What Is Wrong with the Abuser and Why Should I Care?

Some women have asked, "Why should I care about what is wrong with the abuser? That's his problem. I just want to take care of myself."

It is worth knowing what is wrong with the abuser because by doing so, you can:

- Stop wondering if there is something wrong with you.
- Stop wondering why the abuser was nice to others and not to you.
- Stop wondering if he planned to abuse you at particular times. The only people who plan to abuse, enjoy being abusive and lying, and have no remorse are sociopaths—about 3 percent of the population.
- Stop wondering why he would try to control you, the one who loved him.
- Stop thinking you can unravel the mystery about why your abuser abused.
- Stop thinking your abuser could, by will power, stop verbally abusing.
- Stop thinking your abuser is necessarily an evil, bad person.

You would know that there is something wrong with him.

Even if you have left your abuser, it is important to know what is wrong with abusers so that you can let go of any thought such as, "Maybe it's me." "Maybe I said or did something unconsciously to anger him." When you don't blame yourself, it is easier to recover! When you understand what is wrong with the abuser, you stop trying to explain yourself, fix yourself, be different, or ignore it so it won't happen again. Additionally, by knowing what is wrong with the abuser, you will recognize abuse in the future, no matter how covert it is.

The following story, one of thousands of similar stories, illustrates the fear that long-term verbal abuse creates and summarizes the above points that are so fundamental to recovery.

Married for over twenty years, a woman related that when her spouse was away, by the second day after his departure, she started to relax from the hypervigilant state she was always in. She never knew what would set him off, anger him, or cause him to unexpectedly zap her with a cutting comment. She wanted to know, "What am I doing wrong? He isn't like that with other people."

I explained to her, "You are doing nothing wrong. It is your very personhood that sets him off. When you show up with a thought, question, or suggestion, he can't find 'the rest of himself.' He is so merged into you that he lives as though *you* were the rest of him. When you don't move, walk, talk, or think like the rest of him is 'supposed to' at any given moment, he feels attacked. His unconscious, so to speak, is screaming, 'Where did the rest of me go!'"

A case in point: Mel Gibson allegedly said to his former girlfriend, "You insult me with every look, every breath, every heartbeat."

If his partner's existence was insulting to him, it is not difficult to imagine that at some unconscious level he might have meant: *Your personhood is a threat to my connection to reality itself because I live within you, via my projected self. When you show up in your body, by your* look, *your* breath, *even your* heartbeat, *I can't find the rest of myself. There isn't room for my lost self to reside in you along with the real you. So, when you show up, part of me is gone. Wow, where did the rest of me go? I'm hung out to dry. That is why your existence so assaults me. No wonder I attack. I am getting back at you for existing where I am supposed to exist.*

Abusers will respond with anything from irritation to rage if their partner does not match their projection. *Controlling People* explains what this lost "self" projected into the partner is all about.

Abusers Define Their Partners

To further clarify, let's look at what abusers do. No matter how overt or covert the abuser is, all verbal abusers do one thing universally. That one thing is this: abusers define their partners *as if they were living within them* and knew their inner world: what they are, their motives, thoughts, feelings, and so forth.

Abusers behave as though they *were* their partner, child, friend or acquaintance. That is, abusers act as if they know what another person is, thinks, needs, feels, wants, and is doing, did, and should do.

In summary, when someone defines you in any way, tells you what you are ("too sensitive," "stupid," "hopeless"), or actually tells you your motives (for example, "You're trying to start a fight," "You want to win," "You want to have the last word"), he or she is behaving as if he or she were you, or were God!

In normal discourse among people, if you criticize someone, you are usually quick to apologize when you realize that you have no right (unless invited) to critique the other.

If verbal abuse has slammed into your consciousness with assaults that attempt to erase your own awareness of who you are and how you perceive yourself and even your existence, then verbal abuse may brainwash you into believing that you actually are a person who *is* too sensitive.

This is what is wrong with verbal abuse and why I support your victory over it.

A Partner Defined as Nonexistent

Some abusers define their partners as nonexistent, so they withhold a response to any question or comment. They don't hear or see their partners. The partner holds the abuser's projection so the abuser is certain the partner already knows the answer to the question. The abuser seems unable to face the fact that the partner is actually a separate person. The abuser is unconsciously driven not to lose the part of himself projected into his partner. Consequently, he will deny the separate existence of his partner.

Partners experience this phenomenon as feeling like a wall seems to exist between them. Of course, the partner is not really in a partnership with her mate. In fact, she is in what seems to be a relationship doomed to loneliness.

Recovery from an Abusive Interaction

Recovery takes an in-depth understanding of what verbal abuse is. This is why I ask callers to read all the books and it is why I am writing this one.

A client said almost exactly what dozens of other clients have said: "I know what verbal abuse is, but when I asked my husband, 'Will you please stop calling me names?' he ragingly said, 'Now you're trying to control me!' So, what can I do? I don't want to look like a controller."

She really thought she knew what verbal abuse is and she thought that she had to prove to him that the lie he told her about her motives wasn't true.

What's Happening?

I told her that what her husband said was abusive. Then I explained the abuse like this:

1. He dumped anger on you. Raging at someone is abusive.
2. He withheld an answer. Diverting/withholding is abusive.
3. As if he were a god who knew your motives, he defined them! Defining someone's motives/accusing is abusive.

A brain scan would show that his rage actually records a brain response in her the same as if she were hit on the head. Furthermore, her husband actually told her what her motives were! He told her what she was *trying to do!* Of course, his accusation was a lie told to her about her so it was a blatant abuse.

She had simply asked him to please choose not to call her names. She asked him a question. He chose not to answer and to abuse her three ways in one sentence!

See the Projection

Then I asked her a question, "Do you think that all this verbal abuse was done to *silence* you? If so, *who* was actually indulging in controlling behavior? Was he actually accusing you of something he was doing?"

She realized that he was.

The typical abuser appears to have made the other person a part of his or her own psyche. Abusers act as if they were omniscient while not conscious of their projection. This is why abusers don't feel crazy or irrational when defining another person. And, since, in a godlike way, abusers adamantly declare that they are right, some may automatically assume that anyone who is different from them is wrong, even people of different ethnicities. Thus prejudice is born.

Know and Plan Responses

Possibly the best response to his accusation that diverted her from her question, "Would you please stop calling me names?" would be to ask the question again, and again, until he answered the question. One woman I talked with said she asked a similar question eleven times before her abuser answered it. She, of course, did not respond to his nonsense.

If he said, "no" or "I'll call you what I want," she could choose to leave or use some other response. One client actually served her husband with legal separation papers the next day. This is what men on the online support group for Men Ending Verbal Abuse and Control (MEVAC) call "The SledgeHammer Effect." The link to their site is on *www.verbalabuse.com.* This men-only support group is at this URL: *http://mevac.proboards.com/index.cgi.*

Earlier in the chapter, we talked about responses to verbal abuse that are not useful. Now, let's look at some that can be useful. For example, you could hold up a video camera while repeating the question just to see if his response changes. If not, turn his behavior into an educational video. Or, hold up a video camera, saying, "Would you please repeat that?" (Secure the camera to your waist with a cord and keep it in your pocket so that he can't take it from you.) Keep a cell phone in your other pocket so you can dial 911 if he becomes violent. All will be on camera. He will not be able to say you battered him. He has a choice: to stop the abuse, walk away or speak kindly. Another response could be, "Please, ask me nicely what I was trying to do, because you are not me, and cannot step into my soul and know my motives." Another could be, "I don't want to ever, ever hear you tell me what I am or what I am trying to do again. You aren't me. If you want to know what I am trying to do, please ask me nicely with your happy voice."

Please be aware that most verbal abusers are too smart to physically abuse their partners. If you are around one that does or is about to, call 911 or contact the National Domestic Violence Hotline to get help in your area at 1–800–799–SAFE or 1–800–799–7233.

My point is that this client really didn't *recognize* the abusiveness of her mate's last statement, didn't see it as *his* control tactic, didn't know *what was wrong with him* when he told her, "Now you're trying to control me." It was, in fact, what *he* was doing. She didn't know about verbal abuse and control tactics, or she might have spotted her spouse's abusive behavior and known that she didn't have to defend herself against his accusation. The accusation was simply a lie.

Even if you have left an abuser and are on the road to recovery, knowing what is wrong with a person who has defined you facilitates the process of recovery.

The Terminal Outcome of Verbal Abuse

You must be free from the influence of verbal abuse to heal and recover; this may mean a physical separation. If you have left an abuser, it is important to know that long before you left, the abuser ended his relationship to the real you.

I have seen that verbal abuse has a terminal impact on couple relationships—that is, it results in the end of the relationship—*unless* those who indulge in verbal abuse recognize what they are doing and resolve to do all the work needed to change. Verbally abusive relationships end or are terminated in three primary ways, along with a less common fourth way:

1. At the time in which it occurs, verbal abuse terminates any relationship between two people. The relationship ends when

the perpetrator defines the partner's inner reality because the perpetrator cannot see or hear the real you. The perpetrator is, in effect, saying "I cannot hear or see the *real* you. I am closed off from you."

From a systems perspective, a relationship between two people (or any two living entities) requires that they be open to exchanging information between them. The only way they can do this is to perceive each other as separate people. This exchange can't happen if the perpetrator is closed from the *real* person. The perpetrator may open the relationship later, i.e., be open to a response from the other person when asking a question such as, "Is dinner ready?" The relationship is then open at a superficial level.

2. If there is no true change within the perpetrator, even the appearance of a relationship is doomed to fail, to be terminated, not only in a systemic way, as described above, but also in a legal way if divorce is an option.
3. Verbal abuse may terminate a relationship by the sudden absence of the victim. Here is how. Verbal abuse, covertly or overtly, defines a person's very being. People who are defined negatively from birth on suffer tremendously, although as a child they may adapt to, and normalize, everything happening to them. They may, then, as adults, be depressed and confused. They may not even realize that they are being verbally abused nor how it is impacting them. A person who has been slammed with verbal abuse may feel like giving up, like dying. Their emotional pain and mental anguish may be so great they self-medicate with drugs or alcohol. They may have had no name for what they suffered.
4. Over time, verbal abuse compromises the immune system of anyone it targets. Any illness brought on or exacerbated by stress can lead to an early death.

Nearly all of the people I've heard from feel like they *might* die if they leave their abusive relationship; they also say they are sure they *will* die if they stay in their abusive relationship. Some choose to separate and see if their spouses do all the work to recover. Whatever they choose, I believe that much of the meaning and purpose of their lives must become their recovery and the new lives they create.

3

Recovery, Discovery, and Beyond

One way to think of your recovery, and even the rest of your life, is as an exciting adventure of self-discovery. Besides recovering any lost self-confidence, self-esteem, serenity, and peace of mind, you will discover that life itself, at any age, can present new insights, gifts you never knew you had, and the power within you to be more than you ever dreamed, more than you ever expected. This is the process of self-discovery. And, self-discovery is bringing to consciousness that which is within you.

Increasing Self-Definition

Having been defined in some or many ways, over a brief or long period of time, or having been deprived of the opportunity to pursue an interest you'd been inclined to pursue, recovery includes the intention to pursue your interests and to discover just who you are. You may ask yourself, "What do I most admire and am inspired by in others? Is it the work or accomplishments or performance of an artist, musician, athlete, singer, actor, architect, speaker? Is there some way I can activate that in my life? If I can't be an athlete, can I coach a child? If I don't think I can sing, can I take some singing lessons?"

You may also learn more about yourself by checking out your personality type by taking quizzes offered in books and online. The Internet offers many resources for this. Search, "What is my personality type" to find out more.

Similarly, you may also explore your best career options by searching the Internet for everything from best-paid careers to the best careers for your personality type.

Another way you can know more about yourself is to know your IQ. This measurement is based on the cultural view of intelligence; it is not, for example, a measure of musical intelligence. Many people have been led to believe that their IQ is low because their thoughts, views, plans, or expressions have been constantly countered. When asked to stop, some abusers say, "I'm just playing the devil's advocate," as if justifying their ongoing attempts to erase their partner's mind. Some simply tell their partners that they can't communicate.

I spoke with a woman years ago whom I still remember as extraordinarily eloquent. She would mention something and then flow into a perfect and beautiful metaphor to clarify her meaning. I couldn't keep myself from saying, "I think you'd be a really great public speaker." She responded, "My husband constantly told me, 'You can't put two words together.'"

Abusers Can Heal, Too

If you realize that you have perpetrated verbal abuse over time, been the agent of a legacy of verbal abuse handed down through generations where you were defined as born to be seen and not heard, born to suppress your pain, born to be perfect when perfect wasn't good enough, you may recover the self that was hammered out of you. You will have much to do, as I have often told my clients, but is there anything else more important? If you have indulged in verbal abuse on a regular basis, I hope you will begin to heal from your childhood and the culture that has told you to toughen up, lose your emotional intelligence, and erase your empathy.

If you have been abusive, you may, with therapy and support, stop expecting a partner to be that which was lost within you: the warm, empathic, receptive, emotionally intelligent, intuitive, sensitive part of you—as well as, if you are a woman, the doing, active, decisive part of you, that is, the rest of you. You may integrate your lost self. Your anger may dissipate that someone is not the rest of you, does not always want what you want, do what you anticipate, know what you know, think what you think, say what you expect, and know what you meant—as if s/he were the rest of you. You may then experience your partner as a separate person, a real person. You may then, in time, be able to respond to a question, not with another question, nor with irritation, nor with anger, nor with sarcasm, nor silence, but with an actual answer. You may, in fact, be able to see and hear the Other.

You may remember what happened to you in childhood, but not understand how your childhood experiences set you up to define your partner's very being. You may never think of yourself as controlling. Here's an example.

An anonymous man called me. We had the following conversation.

"Hi, I just read your book. Now I know why I threw my wife to the ground."

"Really. What happened?" I asked.

"Well," he replied, "I got home from work early and I love to cook. So, I was cooking up a storm, had all the burners going. Then my wife came home. She said, 'Hi' and I said, 'Hi.' Then she looked down at the mail on the counter, and started thumbing through it to see if there was any for her. I got so mad I went over and threw her to the floor."

"Really?" I said.

He said, "Yeah, now I know why. I just read *Controlling People.* My dream woman was going to come over and offer to help me with the cooking."

His dream woman (projected feminine side—the lost part of himself) disappeared before his very eyes. Real woman appeared. All he knew then was the rage he felt at losing the rest of himself.

He knew he had lost so much of himself that he acted crazy. He also knew that there was a lot of work ahead to begin to recover himself—maybe years.

Avoid Contact with Abusers

If you have been in a verbally abusive relationship, or are in one now, or have been defined by a family member, friend, culture, or religion, you can best begin to heal the wounds of the past, erase the weapons of words used against you, and focus on your own healing if you have no contact with whomever abused you. If you are in a marriage, then a planned separation may work for you if the abuser gets trauma therapy for whatever traumas disconnected him from his emotionally intelligent, empathetic self. If you have shared custody of children, see if you can set up a safe exchange of any children. This allows you to drop off the children with someone you know and have checked out, and for your ex to pick them up a few minutes later, so that you do not have to encounter him. Try to keep all communication about the children only, and via e-mail or text if possible.

I spoke with a caller today who said, "Where can I go to get better? I'm a wreck." So, I asked her a few questions. "When is the last time you saw the person who abused you?"

"Yesterday," she said. "He came over to give me a check."

I suggested that she see if she could have any payment paid directly to her bank account or set up a new account for that purpose.

I learned that her former husband came over frequently to see his two children who were in their late teens. One had a car and could drive. There was no reason for him to be in her house. Seeing the person who had so tormented her re-traumatized her.

Recovery is the restoration of something lost. Verbal abuse creates loss. It robs people of their sense of self, their confidence, happiness, self-esteem, self-awareness, serenity, ability to trust, peace of mind, and almost their minds.

4

A Positive Perspective

If life and the difficulties people experience can be seen from a whole new perspective, then meaning and purpose can arise out of the ashes of near destruction. Being blamed, defined, and deprived can impact anyone's confidence, expectations, and aspirations. In a world, or a relationship, that defines you, the process of recovery becomes a process of self-discovery. Knowing that there are ways to recover from the impact of verbal abuse and to grow beyond imposed limitations enables you to see how an abusive relationship is, in fact, no relationship at all. However, the goal of recovery is attainable. It is victory over the influence of verbal abuse.

It is never too late to recover and to make meaning of the nightmare of a verbally abusive relationship. Some partners have experienced years of abuse while trying to figure out what was wrong—and while thinking that something was wrong with them. Some think that picking the wrong person shows that there is something wrong with them. However, anyone can marry a seemingly fine person, then find there is a cold or raging mate. The abuser's switch in behavior is very common.

With faith and hope for herself and others, a woman who had lived in fear and trauma for *sixty-four* years contacted me. She told me that she had kept hidden everything that happened to her, so that no one, not even her children, would know how she had been treated. She asked me to share this and any of her story, if it would help others.

She had been with her abuser since she was a teen. All those years she believed it would hurt her children to know her agony. And if she went to the hospital from the assaults, she imagined that she would be on the front page of the newspaper.

We have a new perspective now—a positive one. Some women even hope to get the truth *into* the newspapers, but in those days, victims felt responsible for the relationship, as if the abuser's shame were their own. This woman thought if she were a good enough wife, the abuse wouldn't happen. He told her that he wasn't going for counseling and that "If they could straighten me [the wife] out, everything would be fine." She had been knocked unconscious, had chunks of hair pulled from her head, was beaten frequently and was verbally abused to the point of brainwashing. Her husband sent the children out to do some task before he beat her so they did not see it. But he did abuse his four children and the oldest ended up with flashbacks.

Because her own childhood had been abusive, all she wanted to do all those years was show love to people so they would not suffer. In the end, it was her hope to help others that gave her the courage to begin leaving and to contact me.

Generally speaking, the difference between a partner who stays in an abusive relationship for years and one who leaves in the first few years is their childhood experience. If the partner grew up in an abusive family atmosphere, the partner will be inclined to endure the abuse longer. Everything is their fault, they learn from infancy on.

On the other hand, partners who were treated with kindness and respect in childhood usually confront their abuser, see change, or leave much sooner. Other factors that keep partners in abusive relationships are: how overt the abuse is, whether the abuse escalates to physical assault, whether the partner must stay to protect the children, and whether the partner even has a name for what is happening—verbal abuse.

If, like the woman who contacted me after sixty-four years, you have endured years of covert abuse, countering and withholding, or overt abuse, name-calling, and even physical assaults, you will be able to recover and to fulfill the meaning and purpose of your soul. It just requires determination. If you have lived in fear, been on guard against raging verbal assaults, been isolated and penniless, part of your journey will be self-discovery. Partners starting the path of recovery often wonder, as you may wonder, "Who am I? How do people know what they like or can do?" If you endured such a childhood too, you are not alone.

While time heals physical wounds, an antibiotic or bandage may facilitate the healing process. Likewise, when it comes to emotional pain, the healing that time affords reaps more benefits if we apply the antibiotic and bandage of affirmation and positive action. But positive action and affirmation best take place in the context of a positive perspective.

A new perspective on your recovery may help relieve some of your pain. One might be: he was *not capable* of seeing me and hearing me; I did nothing to justify his behavior.

A positive perspective is a lens, so to speak, through which you see yourself as the unique person that you are. No one in the world has your unique combination of gifts and talents. It is imperative that you appreciate and value yourself no matter how anyone has defined you.

"But wait," the partners of abusers have said, "If I'm so unique and I've tried so hard to do the right thing, to be loving and kind, then *why did this happen to me?*"

Why Did This Happen to Me?

This question might be expressed in various ways. For example: Why was I born to this parent? Why did the person who said they loved me switch into an abuser? Why were the kids at school so mean? Why didn't I realize early on what was happening to me? Why was I never good enough for my parents?

Faced with the question, "Why did this happen to me?" a woman told me of the horrors of her life as she had been married to a man who turned verbally abusive and controlling right after they married. She lived a nightmare in pain and confusion always trying to do more and be more to gain her spouse's love, always convinced that somehow, as he so often said, she had said or done something wrong. Both of her parents had been verbally abusive and controlling and she had reasoned, while still a very young child, that if she were only better, they would love her. Her loneliness would go away, and she would stop feeling so much pain. When her now ex-husband was courting her he told her he loved her and had appeared to be just what she was looking for.

She tried to understand why life had seemingly tricked her, why God could let this happen to her. I thought of a story (based on her life) that I am sharing with you now to support you in your own recovery, whether from a difficult childhood or a relationship that you couldn't make work, or, to help you simply to grow beyond where you are now—to be further empowered.

This is the story I told her. It is adapted from my book, *Teen Torment* (Adams Media, Inc., 2003).

A soul was given a choice to come to earth with *many* gifts. The gifts she would be given would be, in every way, inner jewels, brilliant and powerful. They would never wear out nor lose their power.

But with these gifts, she would also be given a task, and the task would be the most difficult of all such tasks because she would be given so many wonderful gifts. It was within her power to decide to come or not. If she didn't come with all the gifts, she could gain them one at a time through many lifetimes.

She was told a bit about her task. She learned that if she came to earth, she would be born in a modern age into a home so backward it would be as if it were not much more than a cold and sterile prison. But, *worse than even that*, to the entire world, the home would appear to fit in with modern times, and with a good neighborhood.

No one would speak kind words. But, *worse than even that*, all the words that would be spoken to her would be lies told to her, about her. (You are worthless. You are nothing. You made me do that. You're just trying to get attention. It's all your fault!)

There would be much work to be done, every day, just to survive. But, *worse than even that*, whatever she would do would not be good enough.

Her parents would hardly ever hear her and would never understand her. They would even say, "I can't understand what's wrong with you," seemingly confirming to her that there was something wrong with her. But, *worse than even that*, she would sense that something wasn't right. But, *worse than even that*, she would have no one to tell. But, *worse than even that*, she would not know what she would tell—what was wrong, even if she knew to whom to tell it.

She decided to come to earth anyway, to have and use her gifts. She forgot all about the time before she came. She was born. She grew healthy and strong although her parents seldom held her, never kissed her, or told her they loved her. And, sometimes they forgot that she was there.

Her father was angry. Her mother called her stupid, even though she was so gifted, she could already read and write when she started school. She studied a lot. She always hoped to discover what it was that seemed to be wrong.

As a child, she could hear music and remember the notes in her mind. Someone from the neighborhood heard her play a piano. She was so musically gifted, she ended up being the only child playing in the town orchestra. But her parents saw her accomplishment as nothing. They said, "She shouldn't call attention to herself that way." Then she didn't.

She painted a picture in school and was so artistically gifted someone bought her painting, but her parents said, "So what?" and she gave away her money, to make someone feel better.

She walked to school feeling awkward, wearing the wrong clothes, not like the other kids, with her head down to hide herself. And, in truth, she was shunned because she was different. The other kids laughed at her, tormented her, bullied her, and she never fought back because she didn't want to hurt anyone.

But, even worse than all their torment, she *knew* she didn't fit in. *Something is wrong with me*, she thought, *even the kids know it*, and so she decided *my parents are right.*

Almost automatically, she knew science and so she spent a lot of time in libraries working and working. It seemed better to be away from home. The library felt better than the home she came from. She wasn't sure why. Maybe, she thought, *I don't want to be around my family because they know something's wrong with me. But they don't understand what's wrong with me.*

Eventually, she met and married a man and made a home, but, not knowing the difference, she had married someone who turned into a different version of her own parents combined. He was as familiar as people at home, but this one said, "I love you." It was a great relief to hear those words. She felt fine for just a little while, because about the time of her honeymoon he stopped saying nice things.

Every minute of every day, she struggled to make her home real and not at all like the home she'd grown up in. She thought of that home as unreal. The man she married almost immediately felt irritated and sometimes attacked by everything about her because she seemed so real and so different from him. Her children loved her and were handsome, beautiful, and talented because they were born with her gifts, but they never heard her play a note. They never saw a bit of her art. They forgot even that she had earned many degrees because she had spent so much time in schools and libraries. She, too, stopped thinking of all she had done. There was so much to do, and she did it all.

She helped her husband develop his career, and he soon had a very substantial income. But, she couldn't always buy what she needed because all the income was hidden, all the checking accounts empty, and all the credit cards closed. She had only a small allowance. She drove an old car that wasn't safe for her or her children. Her husband didn't care. But the people at the station, where she got gas did care. They put all their extra money together, watched for a good sale, and got her a better car. She never told them about the hundreds of thousands of dollars her husband earned. By then, she was convinced that she only deserved the grocery money he gave her, and if it weren't for her children's safety, she would not have accepted the almost-new car.

One day she heard about verbal abuse and thought of the hundreds of times (maybe thousands) that her husband had blamed, accused, trivialized, judged, ordered, and yelled at her—even saying what she had heard in childhood: "You are worthless. You are nothing. You made me do that. You're just trying to get attention. It's all your fault!" The only difference between what she'd heard in childhood and what he said was that he said, "You're being a drama queen," instead of "You're trying to get attention."

I'd talked with her before, but on this day I told her the story. Then I said, "This is your story.

You came with the gifts of an athlete, the gift of music to be a child prodigy, the gift of vision to design, the gift of health to have fine children, and the gift of intelligence to become anything. These gifts are like jewels within you. But you received them along with a task.

Your task is this: to own every gift like a jewel, to value yourself, and to know yourself, no matter what anyone says or how they mistreat you."

I asked, "Can you see how I might see that the purpose and meaning of your life is to gather your jewels and own them? Then use them to see that you are priceless, no matter what anyone says or does."

There was never anything wrong with you. But there was something wrong with your abusers.

Knowledge Is the Key

Not everyone has had as difficult a childhood as this woman did. However, no matter how great your childhood was, you could be caught up in a relationship that either suddenly or gradually becomes abusive. But you need not worry that you will be duped for long. Not if you have all the knowledge of what verbal abuse is, as well as what is wrong with the verbal abuser.

When dating, anyone can meet an abuser or even hear some abuse, but a wise and empowered person will not be around the abuser for long. The key to avoiding verbally abusive and controlling relationships is to remember the adage that battered women have heard from those who shelter them. "Hit me once, shame on you. Hit me twice, shame on me."

Women have asked, "How do verbal abusers manage to look so nice and friendly to everyone else? How do they know how to fool all our friends?"

My usual reply is, "They don't have to learn anything to look good to others. They look good to others because their lost self is not projected into others. The other person is not 'the rest of' them."

I now illustrate this point. "Please try looking at it this way. No other person insults the abuser by his or her look, breath, or heartbeat. No other person is his or her partner."

Sociopaths, not to mention the everyday abuser, can even fool therapists and psychologists, so of course, they can fool neighbors, family, friends, and colleagues. One man even fooled the United States Navy and got an invite to an inaugural ball, wearing an unearned Medal of Honor under the guise of being an admiral. He had only served nine months in the navy years before (see the full story in *A Dance with the Devil: A True Story of Marriage to a Psychopath* by Barbara Bentley).

Recovery with Faith and Determination

It is important to know that no matter what you have been told about yourself, if you use your abilities, always doing your best, you will discover through experience who you are and of what you are capable. It may take great faith in yourself to persist when you are filled with doubt, when your self-esteem has eroded or you have adapted to a hostile and toxic relationship, childhood, or culture. But by doing all you can to value yourself, you can overcome the impact of verbal abuse. One woman said, "Even at times when I have nobody but myself, I know I love myself enough to create my own miracles."

Many people have been negatively defined by someone else or by their culture. Many are unsure of themselves, or wondering if they have any gifts, or wondering how they will survive their pain, or overcome the negative messages they've internalized, or their economic circumstances, or their exhaustion, or dissolve their fears, or figure out what to do next, or regain their confidence, or get a good night's sleep. If you wish to grow beyond where you are now, your resolve to do so will serve you well.

A Survivor's Story of Her Faith in Herself and Her Resolve to Keep on Her Path

I asked a woman who is on a healing journey if she would share some of her story with me for this book on recovery. And she complied. I know this highly intelligent, organized, and competent woman once felt hardly even average and definitely not very competent. After all, she'd grown up being assured that such was the case.

She wrote, "My recovery began when I was forty and realized how my mother enabled the abuse in my life, over and over and over again, until I began to really integrate what I'd learned about abuse. So, I am relatively new to recovery, just five years now. I knew enough to have nothing more to do with my abusive father in my early twenties. I knew enough to leave my physically abusive first husband after he beat me up while I was pregnant. I knew enough to divorce my second husband who continually lied to me and about me, and ganged up on me with my first ex to wrest my oldest children from me. What I didn't know was that all along, there was my mother explaining sweetly how it was all my fault and how I could avoid further abuse by changing to the abuser's whims.

"The only thing I've ever truly been able to do is keep moving forward, taking one step at a time, and putting one foot in front of the other. Daily I find myself, at times, still wishing I wasn't born. Not because I have no worth, not because I don't positively affect people in my life but because each next step is like walking with cement shoes most days. But most people don't have a clue about this regarding me. The few who do have saved me from acting upon the more severe remedies I've contemplated.

"On a daily basis, if you were around me, you would see a sunny smile and instant joy regarding happy things. If things were harsh or difficult, you might see humor or at least a respectful silence rather than a reaction. It takes a lot for me to react and I've had to really think about why this is. Here's the thing. If I were to truly react to acts of abuse/control from another person, I dare say I'd probably be in jail. I had an amazing temper when I was younger and it kept abusers at bay but it also kept loved ones at arm's length. I am trying to balance that as we speak.

"The biggest hurdle thus far is battling the lies people tell about me to each other so they can feel better about the horrible things they do. Of course, I don't even consider that they are right, but still it scares me how few emotions I actually feel. I need to feel safe to have some of the stronger feelings. *Feeling safe isn't something I am used to and continues to be a bit elusive but it is coming along.*

"I have some years to go until my children are off to college. However, I am doing a bang-up job in the meantime supporting them financially and emotionally. I know I am doing the best I can. I am judged harshly for all I don't/cannot do but I know I'm giving it my all and that is all I can do. When my youngest is an adult, I can forever sever any ties with his father. I see a light at the end of the tunnel.

"I love the joy that happens and find myself amazed when others think well of me. I know those that make up lies about me are sick and yet still, still there is a hurting person who needs reassurance, not harsh judgments. The world will never see that poor baby's face, though.

"So when I hear my mother's poisonous talk about how I deserve what I get or how I can alone prevent abuse directed at me, I realize what a charlatan she is and how she schemes and manipulates people. When people close to me are harsh and unforgiving of my human nature I remind myself how much effort I put into *not* being abusive toward others and how hard I try to be clear and caring. In the end, nothing much matters but how I treated someone else and as long as I have rock-bottom treated people the way I want to be treated, any fault found I consider projection. What more can I do but offer first the behavior I'd like to see in return?

"I refuse to be walked on. I refuse to bow and scrape for no good reason. I refuse to be the mat others wipe their feet upon. The behavior I offer others is so much better than that. Yet time and again I was told my standards are too high. I disagree. I am offering the kindness I would like to be treated with, honesty, integrity, and much more. I consider these basic human behaviors ones we extend anyone. Why would I change that and become that which I despise? I wouldn't and I won't."

The processes and affirmations in the following chapters will support you if you are seeking growth, serenity, and fulfillment for any reason. It is my intention that if you were subject to verbal abuse in childhood and/or as an adult, you find the support that works for you. I believe that all of life is about growing awareness.

5

Healing Therapies and More

You are not powerless to deal with sadness, loneliness, and anxiety. In this chapter, you will discover powerful methods to manage your emotions and fears in a healthy way. Even if you feel very sad and lack confidence, there are many things you can do to help yourself, one step at a time. Please remember that the first thing you can do is talk nicely to yourself.

If you remember some negative comment you heard, know that what was said to you is the opposite of the truth. In fact, as you will see, you can find your gifts by knowing this.

Discovering Your Greatest Gift

There is a secret message in verbal abuse. The message is that the negative statements you've heard most about yourself reveal your greatest gifts. Why is this? Simply put, when you are showing up with your greatest gift, you fill your very being with your presence—your uniqueness. For example, if you communicate well, when you are expressing yourself your brilliance comes shining through. You show up in the space where the abuser has projected his or her lost self. The abuser reacts instantly to put you down, to silence you, or to act as if you didn't exist. The abuser does this so there will be, so to speak, space within you for his or her projection. The abuser is most reactive to you when you are being you. The more you show up, the more the abuser feels attacked, rejected, or irritated. Abusers feel this way because they can't find the "rest" of themselves.

To discover your greatest gifts, please ask yourself, "What negative comment did I hear most about myself?" Doing this, clients in consultations have told me, "Oh, I know what it was!"

Here is what some of them heard, and their realizations.

Discovering Your Gifts

What Was Said	The Great Gift
"You're selfish."	Generosity
"You can't communicate."	Eloquence
"You want to win."	Cooperativeness
"Your paintings are crap."	Award-winning artist
"You aren't listening."	Memory of the spoken word

The Power of Contrast

If you contrast the verbal abuse you've heard with what you hear from a healthy person or develop a relationship with a healthy person, you may be shocked to realize not only how irrational the abuser was, but also how unexpected the nonabusive person's behavior is. You may have braced yourself for an angry comment after a simple question, or even remained on guard when doing nothing much at all, simply existing. You may have felt ready to defend yourself if you heard a lot of countering. Or, you may be surprised when someone, especially in a new relationship, asks you for your thoughts, or what you didn't like about some movie or event that you've said you don't care for.

Because they have experienced so much abuse, some survivors feel ready to apologize for everything—almost for existing. As you become clearer and stronger, have success and healthy people around you, these defenses will fade away. It all takes time and determination to do all you can to further your healing and recovery.

What's Normal?

Many people have asked, "What is normal? How bad was the situation I left?" They often mean, "What do a healthy relationship and a healthy family look like?" Partners of people who indulge in verbal abuse have become so used to yelling, the silent treatment, countering, criticizing, or blaming, that they don't know what to expect in new situations, or how to evaluate them. This is especially true if their childhood homes were similarly abusive. However, anyone can find himself or herself in an abusive relationship, even someone coming from a healthy home. The primary difference is that they usually recognize that something is really wrong in their relationship earlier than do those who were abused in some way in childhood. Even then, some may stay and try to "work it out," with no effort on the part of their spouse. In staying, they may become so brainwashed by the abuse, with no name for what is happening to them, and no understanding from the world around them, that they, too, doubt themselves and wonder what is "normal."

In a healthy home, people don't give others the silent treatment, yell and rage at them, talk behind their backs, give orders, refuse to apologize if they make a mistake, or threaten the other.

Helping Your Emotional Self

This powerful practice builds confidence in your inner voice. It is a process that helps you to trust yourself and your intuition, to nurture yourself, and feel supported from within. This practice works best if done three or four times a day. Many of my clients have told me how much better they felt after practicing it for even just a few weeks. On the surface it may seem like you are talking to yourself and you might wonder, "How can this help me?"

It helps because you will be deprogramming yourself from the negative input you've heard and you will be bringing in a kind of archetypal energy of the "good mother" and the "good father." Archetypes are like patterning principles within human consciousness. Everyone recognizes the archetypes of "hero," "heroine," "outcast," "scapegoat," "villain" and so forth. If you focus on one, like, say, "outcast"—saying to yourself—"nobody likes me," you may bring in that energy and start to feel like an outcast. If you talk to yourself in the way described below, you will bring in the archetypal energy of the good mother and the good father. The outcome for those who practice this is that they do not feel alone. They feel safer, more confident, stronger and, therefore, more able to manage their life. They are happier.

In this exercise, you will be visualizing or imagining your own emotional self. For example, although you can't see your memory, you might think of your memory in different ways. Some people visualize their memory as a Rolodex or a file cabinet. Similarly, you can't see the part of yourself that creates your dreams, but you might say your dreams come from your "dream maker" and then imagine what your dream maker looks like. Likewise, your emotional self might be thought of, visualized, or imagined as a young child. If you see your emotional self symbolized as a young girl, you can be there for her in a way that possibly no one in your life ever was. (Males visualize a young boy.) Here is how to do it.

Your own emotional self, symbolized as a young girl, is trusting and vulnerable. She wants you to talk to her in an encouraging way. Although supportive family and friends may bolster her up, only you can do the inner work that fully empowers her. Not everyone has an understanding family and/or close friends who can be there for them whenever they need to talk. Some people have lost their parents, and some have been isolated from their friends. Even with someone to talk to, talking to your emotional self as a child within is still very important. In many cases, no one really understands what you are going through or have gone through. Whatever circumstance is yours, much of your recovery depends upon you and your determination to create a sense of self that is so strong that you automatically take good care of yourself and build the kind of life you want.

The Process

Visualize or imagine your own emotional self as a young child—so darling, vulnerable, and trusting. If you are male, visualize a little boy and change the references from "she" to "he."

Ask her how she is feeling; talk to her in the kind voice you would use talking to a child. She will be feeling what you're feeling. Whatever she says, acknowledge her feeling and tell her you'll take care of her. Here is a sample script.

You: *Hi, honey, how are you feeling?*

Your Emotional Self: (For this sample, let's say she says, "lonely.") *I'm feeling lonely.*

You: *Of course, you're feeling lonely. It's okay. I'll take care of you.* (Explain to her why she feels this way. Use whatever explanation comes to you. One might be, "You're feeling lonely because I haven't paid any attention to you." Or another might be, "You're feeling lonely because I've been telling you, 'Get over it.'") *You're feeling lonely because your life has changed and there's no one around to share things with.* (Tell her again that you'll take care of her.) *It's okay, honey. I'll take care of you.* (Up until now you've drawn in the archetypal energy of the great good mother—kind, caring, and empathetic. Now, with the next statement you'll be drawing in the energy of the great good father giving her a hopeful solution.) *Here's what we'll do!* (Take whatever answer comes to you, as one surely will. Here are some samples.) *Let's make a list of everyone we know and invite them to an open house party.* (Or another answer might be, *Let's search all the organizations, associations, groups, and classes online that are focused on our interests or goals. Then we'll contact them and join what we want.*) *We can do that now. Let's go.* (Notice how she feels now.)

After reading through this process above, I recommend rereading only the sentences in italics. This is how it will sound when talking to your inner child.

Managing Overwhelming Sadness

When a relationship ends, many people go through a time of grieving the loss of what they hoped they would have. This is an essential part of healing. Sometimes, however, the feeling of sadness is overwhelming and there is no way to deal with it at the moment. Maybe you are at work or involved in other responsibilities.

If you are suddenly overwhelmed with a deep sadness, triggered by a memory or experience such as walking out to your car or walking into your home and feeling completely alone, feeling like dying, but definitely not suicidal, here is a process that helps most people overcome the emotional pain generated by verbal abuse. (Feeling suicidal requires a call for medical help.)

In this process, you will be moving energy out of your emotional center, one inch above your navel, at the center of your energetic body, and up to your chest.

This is very quick to do and works best if done the moment you notice an overwhelming feeling.

Tighten or clench in your stomach muscles so your tummy is as flat as you can make it. Breathe up high into your chest while you pull your shoulders back. Now take a breath, close your mouth, and pant as rapidly as you can through your nose, in and out, very fast for five or ten seconds. While panting say to yourself something like, "I'm okay, I can handle anything," or "I'll be fine, I'm great at taking care of me. I'm strong." Do the breath/affirmation process again, and notice if the feeling is gone or no longer overwhelming.

Managing Anxiety and Panic

When people are traumatized, if they cannot process and recover from the trauma, they may suffer from post-traumatic stress disorder (PTSD). Their sleep may be disturbed, and/or they may become exhausted. They may spend hours going over incidents trying to understand what happened like an endless stream of circular thoughts going over and over the traumatic event. They may feel anxious and may even begin to have panic attacks.

People can be traumatized by a sudden shocking experience like an auto accident or physical assault. They can also be traumatized by verbal assaults. If over time, the shock, pain, and confusion of these assaults build up, anyone experiencing verbal abuse or the isolation of the silent treatment may develop PTSD.

Generally, however, as long as you believe you can get the abuser to be kind and stop the abuse, your anxiety may be kept at bay. In any case, if you leave the abuser, any future contact can be re-traumatizing.

If you are dealing with some anxiety or panic attacks, you can manage them partially or completely with the breathing process I describe below. However, if you have reoccurring symptoms and do not see them lessen in frequency, intensity, or duration, then consult a doctor for further help.

Before practicing this breathing exercise, which is the opposite of the one for managing sadness, let's look at anxiety and panic attacks. There are three different ways a person might react to fear: fight, flight, or freeze. Freeze is most common if there is an overwhelming feeling of powerlessness along with the experience of fear. When one feels powerless, one is unable to fight, and flight is very difficult. Feeling frozen, unable to move or leave can bring on panic, which can immobilize you.

A woman who feared her father's verbal abuse and rages, and who lived thousands of miles away from him, heard that he had convinced her former therapist that she should communicate with him. She'd had no contact with her father for over a year, but found out that her father had approached her former therapist and he (the therapist) now believed that her father had been truly kind to her. All this left her feeling threatened and powerless. She suffered panic attacks because she feared that with the therapist's support her father would find her and would verbally abuse her again. She has begun coming out of her panic by controlling her breathing in the following way.

Instead of bringing your energy up to your chest and out of your emotional center, you do the opposite; you will be pulling the energy out of your upper chest and into your belly. Follow these steps to alleviate your anxiety or panic.

The minute you notice your anxiety or that your heart is palpitating and you're feeling panicky, drop your shoulders, let your chest go down and your belly go out, and breathe deeply so your belly goes out like a baby's does. While you are doing this say to yourself, "I am centered here an inch above my navel. This is my center. I feel my feet on the floor, or back on the chair. I am here in the present moment."

Do this several times, reminding yourself each time to drop and relax your shoulders. If you find that your anxiety and panic are not manageable, talk with your doctor or therapist about what you are experiencing.

The processes above are designed to build a connection between your capable self and your own emotional self, to bring in archetypal support, and to manage emotional pain and anxiety. They are all part of following through on taking care of yourself. Taking this special care of yourself can raise your confidence and increase your self-esteem so you can live the life you want.

Labels, Disorders, Trauma, and Fight, Flight, or Freeze

With the exception of developmental and genetic problems, many of the "disorders" described by the medical profession and the pharmaceutical industry originate with trauma. Consequently, people with behavioral or emotional problems are described as having various disorders. For example, the impact of trauma may make it very hard to focus. When one has trouble focusing, they may be given the label attention deficit disorder (ADD). When someone is traumatized and they experience a rush of adrenalin but they can't run at the moment, they may feel agitated and startle easily. Consequently, they may be described as hyperactive; they have extra energy and no place to put it. Their mind may be racing and they may have trouble sitting still because they can't relax. Then they are labeled with another disorder, attention-deficit hyperactivity disorder (ADHD).

People trying to survive abuse, especially if it occurs in childhood, often suffer from trauma. If so, they may have endless conversations within their own minds, conscious and unconscious drives, feel powerless and rejected as they did in childhood, then feel strong and powerful when they subdue their original feelings of powerlessness. Thus, they may have debates or battles between, "I must be awful" and "I am great." They may look to others to make them feel okay. For example, they may first decide "My new friend is great," but later they may think "My new friend is awful because s/he doesn't make me feel better." They may become hoarders so they won't feel empty. They may believe what an abuser says because no matter how nice they are, the abuser is still defining them as being at fault.

If you have been traumatized or suspect that you have been badly mistreated in childhood, look for support and therapy for PTSD, such as Eye Movement Desensitization and Reprocessing (EMDR), which is described below.

Outside Support and Therapy

Support groups can be a great help to both those who are targeted by verbal abuse and those who perpetuate it.

Since verbal abuse is traumatizing, some people find that getting therapy from a therapist is helpful. If you are not sleeping, having nightmares, flashbacks, feeling paralyzed, developing a fear of people or of going out of the house, or having any other symptoms that are affecting your life, seeing a therapist may be helpful. Look for therapists who specialize in treating your symptoms.

A caution is necessary: If you have spent a great deal of time searching within, focused inward, searching for why someone could have treated you abusively, extended periods of meditation may not be helpful unless you can truly clear your mind and feel good from the experience.

Micronutrients for Mental Health

Dr. Daniel Amen, assistant clinical professor, Psychiatry and Human Behavior, University of California, Irvine, and author of twenty-four books, has documented thousands of SPECT scans (a type of imaging) of the brain and found that emotional trauma causes changes in the brain. As anyone who has experienced verbal abuse—from relationships to school bullying to a raging parent—knows, the emotional pain is extreme. If you find that you are unusually irritable, angry, or depressed, micronutrients may be something you would like to try in addition to any other therapies.

Begin any healing by eating as healthy a diet as possible. Then do your own research into how much the brain requires of oxygen, nutrients, and calories. Search "micronutrients for mental health" on the Internet.

Eye Movement Desensitization and Reprocessing (EMDR)

A woman called me to say how EMDR therapy worked for her. She felt so betrayed and hurt by the actions of her spouse shortly after the relationship ended that even though she had started to move on and was focused on her career, his subsequent behavior left her traumatized. She couldn't seem to get beyond the trauma.

Then she called me to say, "I went to an EMDR therapist I knew, and in a session we addressed that issue. I could hardly believe it. The trauma was gone. I felt fine. I still knew he'd acted like a jerk, but I could let it go and get on with my life."

A man called me whose childhood traumas had left him feeling angry with his son for the smallest thing. He said, "I was doing some EMDR therapy when all of a sudden I smell fresh baked bread. I'm in the kitchen and my Dad just took my toy away. I don't know why. I think 'cause I'd dropped it from my high chair. I felt like I did then. The feeling just went through me. Now I can understand my son and I have a lot more patience with him."

Intensive trauma therapy is so important for anyone who has indulged in verbal abuse because verbal abusers almost always have been abused in childhood. I recommend EMDR therapy. Trained therapists can be found at EMDRia.org. This is the international association.

Emotional Freedom Technique (EFT)

A client said that she had been in a relationship with a man she thought was her soul mate. They started to date and a couple of years passed. She was very kind and thoughtful with him. Then, suddenly he turned very mean, very angry, and sometimes very silent. She struggled to bring him to his senses. And sometimes he seemed like his old self, and then suddenly he wasn't.

She called me to tell me that after she ended the relationship, she would walk into a room in her home, and "see" him there. After practicing Emotional Freedom Technique (EFT), she was relieved of his memory and the impact he had on her.

Somatic Experiencing®

This is an experiential kind of therapy that has helped people with trauma. I learned about it from a woman recovering from verbal abuse. Here is some of what she wrote to me:

"I am seeing a practitioner of Somatic Experiencing and feel it is the missing link in my therapy and healing. After years of therapy of various kinds, one somatic-experiencing session had me feeling vastly different.

"I unfroze physically. I felt sensations in parts of my body that I had not felt in a long time. I suddenly felt physically affectionate toward loved ones, as well as experiencing joy and energy I hadn't felt for years. My mood and sleep improved a lot. I am suddenly able to make plans and look for work.

"I also discovered I am no longer under my husband's spell. I see his behavior much more clearly than I ever had before. Where I had intellectually understood the situation, I now really *feel* and *believe* that I am not responsible for him or his behavior."

Somatic Experiencing was introduced by Dr. Peter Levine in his book *Waking the Tiger*. It is used to remove two kinds of trauma, one that involves a shocking, traumatizing incident such as an earthquake and another one that is ongoing, such as a child deprived of necessary contact or nurturance.

Narrative Therapy

The therapist who practices narrative therapy helps the client to see that whatever the problem is, there are times, or have been times, when the problem did not override his preferred behavior and self-image. Eventually the client doesn't identify with the problem, such as "I am hopeless," but rather sees that there have been moments that show that he is not hopeless and that the problem of hopelessness is something he can overcome. By asking questions, the therapist helps the person see that there have been exceptions to the problem.

A client may say, "I've never been happy," only to recall from the therapist's questions that he did, indeed, feel happy at a particular event. The client can then begin a process of overcoming the problem and building a sense of self that does not include the problem but is successful in overcoming it. To learn more about narrative therapy simply search it on the Internet as there is a great deal of information available.

Hypnotherapy

Some people find hypnotherapy a great support to counseling since they can recall incidents that they have suppressed and that block them from clarity about themselves and about how they have been treated.

Here is how a licensed marriage and family therapist and certified hypnotherapist explains hypnotherapy:

"A hypnotic state is a common, naturally occurring state of relaxation in which the conscious mind is relaxed so that the unconscious mind is more easily accessible. In hypnotherapy, a hypnotic state is induced, after which suggestions can be offered to the unconscious mind and issues can be explored using the creative power of the unconscious. The use of hypnotherapy allows us to access the powerful resources of the unconscious mind; to connect with our best or higher self; to delve beneath whatever conditioning or programming we have received in our lives; to access our inner being; and to uncover and process blocks that may interfere with the expression of our unique, genuine, individual, radiant selves. Hypnotherapy can be a powerful tool for healing and personal growth." —Catherine Young, MFT, CHT

For more information about hypnotherapy, visit her site *www.cyoungmft.com.*

In the process of hypnotherapy, subjects can relax enough to focus with greater awareness and greater intensity on their inner world. And it helps them to accept strengths that they may not have recognized because they were so diminished by their abuser.

To receive a directory of hypnotherapists near you, contact the American Society of Clinical Hypnosis at *www.asch.net*, the Society for Clinical and Experimental Hypnosis, *www.sceh.us/index.htm*, or the American Association of Professional Hypnotherapists, *www.aaph.org.*

Biofeedback

Biofeedback uses technology to give you information on how relaxed you are, and how you can determine what triggers stress. For example, as you consciously relax and you see your relaxed level going up, you learn to put yourself into a state of relaxation. There is information on the biofeedback program at the University of California at Davis. This link takes you to the UC Davis Stress and Wellness Clinic: *http://caps.ucdavis.edu/stress/resources.htm.*

Healing the Spirit

Sinead Flanagan, PhD, a healer who specializes in mind-body healing/transformation, contributes the following: "I have been working in the field of healing and teaching for over fifteen years. While doing hands-on healing for clients with physical and emotional pain and teaching workshops, I receive all sort of information from the body—from the root of their physical ailments or disease to a career change. These strong messages are soul messages urging the client to listen and follow the guidance. I have found that those who chose to suspend fear of the unknown and follow their soul's guidance healed easily and lived much happier lives—from the abused wife who chose freedom over victimhood to the lawyer who became a carpet cleaner. Those who clamped their hands over their ears and continued to resist became more unwell and unhappy.

"The reason we don't want to hear this gentle voice is fear. Fear of what it will demand of us. Fear of what we may have to give up. Fear that it will contradict our beliefs. Fear that we don't have what it takes. But this is one truth of healing: It will never demand more than we can give. The problem is that usually we either think we can't have whatever it is—or we don't consciously know what it is we want.

"That's where I come in: It's very easy for me to read someone's body and see what it's trying to tell them. However, you can hear what the soul is trying to tell you. Get still and *listen*. Most people are either afraid to hear the message or once they know, they try to negotiate. It is in this resistance that dis-ease develops. Healing is really very simple:

"We heal when we're happy and we're happy when we get what we want. This is what I call 'The Sacred Yes.' It is that sacred space that we inhabit when we listen to the truth of who we really are and say 'Yes! Yes, I can. Yes, I will, Yes, I *am*.'

"When it comes to abusive relationships, I can see energetically that the 'victim' has past wounds that have lowered their ability to recognize a potentially abusive person. Because of the nature of my practice, usually by the time they get to me, they have developed physical ailments or diseases. It is this shaky self-esteem that lowers their vibration so they are an energetic match for an abuser. A victim and an abuser usually find one another—even when (and usually!) the abuser initially shows up as charming and attentive. Also, abuse is not always obvious. It can be subtle but even so, will reinforce unworthiness, which is very wounding to the spirit and eventually the physical body.

"Elizabeth is a client who came to me for healing after suffering two grand mal seizures within hours and nearly dying. She had no history of seizures prior to this episode. I immediately looked for some sort of trigger to this violent episode. After some time, Elizabeth looked me in the eye and mentioned casually that her husband admitted cheating on her and then promptly had a nervous breakdown when she said she could not forgive the infidelity and was leaving him.

"I immediately had an image of a toddler throwing an almighty tantrum—which is literally what Elizabeth's body did. She could not contain her hurt and anger at her husband's infidelity—and she felt trapped in the marriage when he then had the breakdown. When she could not escape the pain, her body exploded into seizures. The pain of betrayal was what needed to be healed, along with her fear of never getting away from him. There is also the 'Being Happy Versus Being Good' syndrome evident here: What kind of wife would leave a sick husband? On the other hand, what kind of wife would stay in an unhealthy marriage that was literally making her sick? Unfortunately, Elizabeth did.

"And then there is Claire, who showed up in my office looking fatigued and doubtful. She was frustrated and increasingly fearful about her ill health. She, like many clients, came to see me after doing the rounds of doctors and medications—to no avail.

"When I asked Claire what she wanted, she told me in a resigned and defeated tone, 'I want to get rid of these crippling migraines.' However, what I heard was, 'I need out of this marriage and I'm terrified.' Claire had been struggling with severe migraines for over two years, so severe that she would black out. She had been struggling in an abusive marriage for much longer.

When we looked at the pattern there was a consistent theme: the migraines would always flare up at the weekend—when Claire's husband was around the house.

"I find that feeling trapped causes all sorts of serious diseases. Often people don't know that they're in a jail of their own making, that they hold the key. In Claire's case, she knew she wanted out of the marriage but didn't believe she could survive and take care of her two young children on her own. Caught between a rock and a hard place, the fear that this was her lot in life was causing crushing pain in her head.

"I cannot emphasize enough that whatever your situation is right now, you can change it and what you need most is the support of people who can hold your hand through the process, reminding you constantly that you can do it, that and a little faith.

"When I gently suggested that the real pain was her husband, Claire broke down. While it was painful for her, there was also great relief to be seen, to feel validated that the emotional pain of her marriage was very real. It literally was *not* all in her head! I told Claire the truth of her illness immediately because I knew she was strong enough and courageous enough to hear it at that moment and that it would immediately begin her healing process. I worked on her several times to continue clearing out the fear and, at a deeper level, the unworthiness that had magnetized such a partner in—and kept her there so long. The migraines stopped three weeks after the first healing and six years later have never returned. Almost four months after her first healing Claire separated from her husband. She is happy and healthy today. While the relief of no migraines has been wonderful, the real healing that happened was that Claire realized that she is not that unworthy, lost little girl she once was.

"I have long since known that the body believes what the mind believes. I can see the moment in my clients when they realize that they genuinely can heal. Their face changes, their eyes light up, the realization zings through the body and every single cell turns over with this new and exciting knowledge. And so, the body heals.

"Mary had been struggling with depression and lupus for over nine years. Her healing process would have meant leaving a lousy husband and developing her own bakery business, which gave her the most inspiration and joy. Everything changed about Mary when she talked about her ideas for this bakery—from the delicious cakes to the delightfully artsy decor of the bakery.

"The first time she showed up for a healing she actually told me that she could not heal and live the life of her dreams 'because I'm a Scorpio!' What? I roared laughing. That was one of the best Victim stories I've ever heard and I've heard plenty. Now I may not know much about astrology but I do know that that's a crock of shit. Just like every archetype, every astrological sign has positive and negative aspects. So please don't ever show up in my office and tell me that your sign is the reason you 'can't' heal.

"When a client shows up in my office who is very attached to her Victim Archetype (and we all have one) and continues to return to the familiarity of that role, I stop working with them until they're ready to trust that the rewards of healing the Victim are greater than the benefits of staying small and powerless. I last saw Mary two years ago and she was as attached as ever to her tired and frustrating role.

"The Victim does not always show up as helpless and fragile. For example, Lynn is a woman in her mid-sixties who came to me with glaucoma. When I placed my hands above her eyes to do a healing, I got a flash of her husband and knew immediately that he was somehow connected to her illness. Afterwards, I asked her about this and she told me that she hated him with a passion but had 'no intention of leaving him and starting all over again on her own.' Lynn went on to tell me about her horror of finding out that her husband had an affair. I had never seen such passion behind hatred. Lynn was truly committed to her role as an angry and self-righteous victim. She was reveling in it.

"The glaucoma developed about a year after she found out about the affair and was getting worse. The truth was that she would rather go blind than see her husband and she was also more attached to hating him than healing. When I explained to Lynn that her soul wanted her to move on and create a new and healthy life on her own, she refused. Her sight has continued to deteriorate and I stopped seeing her because, as I told her, there was nothing I could do to help her.

"So, get still and listen to the soul. What do you want? And while fear may be present—it may even feel overwhelming—do you really want to stay trapped in fear? Know that healing will never ask more than you can give. It is the responsibility of the soul to continue to steer us toward fulfilling our purposes and evolving and growing. Trusting this spiritual compass ensures that we adhere to the highest, most joyful, and loving path. Bumps along the way may be learnt from and healed: They are not roadblocks. The soul always knows what's best for us and truth stays the same. The soul will continue to repeat the same message until you get it." You can find more information on spiritual healing at Dr. Flanagan's site, *http://sineadflanagan.com*.

Internet Resources

You can find information on the Internet about all the abovementioned therapies. If you are depressed, traumatized, sleepless, or suffering from the emotional pain and trauma of verbal abuse, in childhood and/or as an adult, if you feel filled with hopelessness ("It's too late for me to have a life"), guilt ("I should have known this person's behavior would affect my children"), or anger, you can heal.

Here are a few suggestions to facilitate Internet searches for information on a topic and for checking on credible sites.

- Put in only key words such as "domestic violence prevention" and your state. Don't put in long phrases.
- When you see results, skip ads unless they are exactly what you are looking for.
- Notice that most of the credible sites are often in the top ten or twenty results because people hear about them and so they get the most hits, or they may have been established for many years and so become known.
- Read the URL to see what the site is about.
- Sites that show up with .org are usually nonprofit sites and so may be oriented toward public service. Sites that are connected to universities and hospitals or federal or state governments may be more reliable.
- Sites that are put up by writers and columnists that you believe in are more likely to have the information you seek.
- Reliable sites usually include contact information so that you can talk to someone directly for more information.
- Use a site like *www.factcheck.org* for information on current topics.
- Use Wikipedia, the free online encyclopedia, for basic information on many topics. *www.wikipedia.org.*

I hope you will be proactive in finding any support that works for you. Never give up on yourself. After all, how can you give up on who you are? You, as consciousness, arrived here from a Divine Source. This Divine Source of consciousness individuated in you and all other people. You are then a child of God.

6

Achieving Victory over Verbal Abuse

Each person who becomes knowledgeable about verbal abuse and overcomes its influence achieves a personal victory. And as the number of people who achieve this victory increases, our world changes. This change means that all people live in a more conscious, humane world. Individually we have ever-increasing freedom to choose our own path on life's journey. We are less likely to fall under the influence of people who define us. We are not stopped from pursuing our goals and passions because someone criticizes our every achievement or manipulates us into believing we are incapable. We are immune to everything from political maneuverings to TV commercials that normalize name-calling, intimidation, and even violence.

Verbal abuse is like a cloud that can descend not only upon a family but also upon a nation. Dictators and tyrants have gained power by disparaging people, while their behavior went unnoticed by whole populations. By both directly accusing and blaming or by implication, they defined and denigrated others to create fear and false beliefs and thus gain power. In a similar way, a spouse may define his or her partner, and a parent may define a child. Imagine a world where no child grows up in chaos, rage, verbal or physical assaults, or deprivation. As humanity becomes increasingly conscious of the need to protect our earth from assaults upon its resources and atmosphere, we also move collectively toward the understanding that assaults upon the human psyche must end. Awareness is required and healing is the outcome.

Healing is possible. Ultimately, it is victory over the influence of verbal abuse. Victory over verbal abuse can be both a personal goal and a goal for humanity. Kindness and verbal abuse cannot exist in the same place, the same relationship, or the same world. Your personal victory over verbal abuse does, therefore, contribute to the healing of our planet.

With awareness you cannot, like some, be manipulated and controlled by those who would brainwash you into believing that those who are against you are for you, and those who are for you are against you. You will spot fearmongers as well as those who define others with lies, and those who stir up hate and prejudice. If you listen carefully, you will hear verbal abuse on talk shows and newscasts. You will hear someone defining another's motives: "He wants to . . ." or implying that the Other attacks, saying, "I'm safe here from attack . . . ."

Implying that the Other is hateful, lazy, has contempt for people, thinks they are incompetent, or anything else is particularly heinous.

As we achieve victory over verbal abuse, most people will recognize evil implications. For example, a woman with three very young children called me exhausted one day and said that her spouse came home from his office and said sarcastically, "I *worked* all day, what did *you* do?" She still had several hours of work to do. She went on to say that she had his comment on her little video camera as she thought the best thing to do was to "out" him. I agreed.

Start at the Beginning

Most people, when going through separation, divorce, or any other major life change, do feel traumatized and do sometimes find they need to simply rest for some days, get time off from a job, gather their strength to go on. If at this moment you wonder, "What can I do? Where do I start? How do I begin to heal?" here are some suggestions.

Change Your Thoughts from Negative to Positive

Begin where you are and recognize the freedom you have to change your thought patterns. Every thought generates a feeling. This is why it is so important to notice what you are feeling, and then ask yourself what you were thinking. This is the thought to change. If, for example, you were thinking, "I feel worse every day," change the thought to, "I am getting stronger, clearer, more confident, and able every day."

Talk to Your Emotional Self

If a sad and despairing feeling arises seemingly on its own, without your having thought anything, it is likely that the feeling arose from a sound, a song, a circumstance, or event that re-traumatized you. Remember that you are not alone and that you can comfort your emotional self, even possibly be able to explain to her why she is sad and how you will take care of her. You will find a process in Chapter 5 that will help you talk with your emotional self.

Establish Order in Your Life

For everything, there is a time and a place; at least that is the faith you can build in yourself. If you find your home is reflecting some inner chaos, and you want to reduce the chaos, take small steps. If you have children, they may leave their own rooms a mess, but your home is yours and kids can keep their doors shut. Your desk, your home including closets and drawers can be as simple and neat as you want—a goal to enjoy as you reach it at your own pace.

Order is all about the physical things in your life, from files and bills to the kitchen counter to your closet. A friend once said, "If you have all the physical things done, you can better handle the emergencies and crises that may come up." Establishing order is helpful for other reasons, too. Clutter is distracting, to say the least, and it is a time-stealer if you have to spend *your* time searching for something that was out of order.

When your home, no matter how small or how large, is free from abuse and you can make it your own, please take pleasure in making it beautiful for yourself and any children you may have. Even ten or twenty minutes a day spent doing something extra to have order and beauty around you will make a difference. Doing so can be healing because by acting on your own behalf, without reference to another, your confidence and self-esteem will grow.

Establish Routine

Routine is all about time. How you use your time and the kind of schedule you keep. Time is your personal resource. Establishing a schedule for yourself helps build a sense of security within. You are taking care of you! This doesn't mean that it isn't flexible, but serves in general as a guideline you follow. Some people find it helpful to put their personal routine into their calendar. Of course, appointments are not so flexible, but if you schedule your appointments on Mondays, you not only know that you will be making them because you have set aside time to do that, but also, you will know when your personal schedule might coincide with, for instance, an opening at the dentist's.

Growing into Meaning, Purpose, and Personal Power

The effort millions of people make to bring peace and joy into their lives is, I believe, the very meaning of our lives—to bring "heaven to earth." They would see a more conscious world rise up from the difficulties they've endured. As we consciously expand our own awareness, appreciate our value, and take care of ourselves and those entrusted to our care, we do indeed gain personal power.

This is the power of consciousness that endures and overcomes the unconsciousness of those who would define us as less than we are. Yes, defining others is a sign of unconsciousness because it is *just plain senseless*. So, I invite you to resolve with confidence and determination to affirm yourself daily. The affirmations are coming up in Part 2. It is just ahead. It is designed to fortify you against the slings and arrows of JPS (Just Plain Senseless) behavior.

Part 2

Weekly Affirmations

This part gives you the opportunity to be proactive on your own behalf. As if you were the most holy of healers, you may choose to actively take in the wisdom here, handed down through time, and to internalize it; that is, to breathe it in and to let it infuse your consciousness with health and well-being.

In time, your continuing growth can inspire others both by example and by the knowledge you have to give. As we come closer to living in a world without verbal abuse, we come closer to a world without war.

7

A Journey Through Time, One Week at a Time

Can you commit to five or ten minutes a week toward your own growth and personal empowerment? This section contains fifty-two affirmations, one for each week of the year. I encourage you to repeat each week's affirmation throughout the week so that it becomes part of your inner self-talk, a resource you can rely upon.

A message follows each affirmation to assist you in applying it to your life. Following the message there are blank lines for your personal notes. If you jot down what you were thinking and doing and how the affirmation helped, by the time you come back to the beginning after a year, you may be astonished by your increased confidence, satisfaction, and inner peace.

I invite you to commit to using the fifty-two weekly affirmations following this section. They are designed to dissolve the impact of verbal abuse, which, over time, has a tremendous effect on all who are subject to it. Though I know your life is busy and complex, please take just a few minutes per week to read the affirmation and message. During the week whenever you encounter a feeling of frustration, indecision, sadness, or any other upsetting feeling, allow the affirmation to flash through your mind and notice how you can apply it.

In relationships, those who have suffered the oppression of verbal abuse may not have known what was wrong. Most have no name for what is happening to them when it occurs, and most try to get the irrational person to behave rationally. Most hear double messages, "I love you" and "You're too sensitive (or crazy, etc.)." As their struggles continue, their mental anguish, emotional pain, lost confidence, self-doubt, sadness, and confusion increase. They may also suffer from stress-related illnesses. To counteract the impact of verbal abuse, each affirmation is designed to increase your serenity, satisfaction, self-esteem, confidence, and clarity.

Whether you have faced someone raging at you, or experienced the silent treatment, whether you've been yelled at, or shunned, I believe these affirmations will assist you.

Each week builds on the last and is followed by a message that expands and clarifies it. The affirmations not only build clarity and confidence, but also work to remove the brainwashing effect of verbal abuse. By that, I mean the internalization or belief that what you have been told about yourself is somehow true and that how you've been treated is somehow your fault. If you repeat an affirmation throughout the day and throughout the week, you will be incorporating it into your thinking and it will be facilitating your healing. This healing brings you back to yourself—the self that you perhaps knew yourself to be years before, or that is hidden within you. Healing is about the process of growth and the strengthening of your personal power. Personal power is not power over others. It is the power to be who you were meant to be—to grow into the person you really are.

If you pursue this healing path with determination, I am confident that you will reap the rewards of increased self-assurance, inner peace, and personal power. And you will gain the satisfaction of living your life with ever-greater meaning and purpose. In other words, your days will lead you toward what psychologists call self-actualization, self-determination, self-realization, or individuation. Generally speaking, this means that, no matter how accomplished and recovered you already are, you will grow even closer to the realization of your full potential in an integrated personality that includes your unique interests, talents, qualities, and capabilities—all that distinguishes you as a unique person, separate from other people's prescriptions of how you *should* be.

The Affirmations Are for Everyone

You need not have experienced verbal abuse in a relationship to benefit from the affirmations. Anyone can use this book to enhance his or her own growth. I doubt that there is anyone who has not been defined in some way, if not at home or at school, then by some segment of the culture, such as through gender or racial discrimination. Some churches define women as unequal because of their gender. Some cultures define men and women as only being capable of specific roles based on their gender. And some groups define those who are different from their group as inferior people. *Mutuality between people does not exist where people negatively define people*—not between significant others in couple relationships, not between family members, not between groups, not between countries, and not between dictators and their "subjects."

Wherever the qualities of empathy, emotional intelligence, and receptivity are denigrated, those who carry those qualities are often dominated and denigrated. People who are devoid of such qualities will usually define receptive, giving, and emotionally intelligent people as *not* what they are, but the opposite of what they are. Empathetic people are called "wusses" or "wimps";

emotionally intelligent people are defined as "too sensitive" or "drama queens"; receptive people are told they "aren't listening."

This is verbal abuse and people who indulge in verbal abuse often try to control or destroy those who have positive qualities. Why? Because they denigrate that which was denigrated within them, and some will even attack *symbols* of what was destroyed within them. Here is an example: An empathetic, kind, emotionally intelligent child is raped in Darfur. Why? Because she represents, or is a symbol of, the very qualities that were denigrated in the soldier who raped her.

From another perspective, when people negatively and consistently define those close to them, such as a partner, child, relative, or friend, telling them what they are, want, feel, not by mistake, but on a regular basis and with no apology, we must ask, "Are they not either behaving as if they were God, or pretending to be God? Are they not taking the name of God in vain?" We might ask, "Are they crazy?" After all, who knows what you are, think, want, or feel, besides you and God?

I personally define Verbally Abusive and Controlling (VAC) behavior as Just Plain Senseless (JPS). This behavior is almost always a result of sudden or ongoing trauma, usually in childhood. I suspect that disorders as defined by psychiatrists are actually human responses to trauma and/or deprivation. And that the symptoms of abuse—fear, sleeplessness, anxiety, attention seeking, self-centeredness, nervousness and so forth—that are treated with drugs are best treated with various trauma therapies.

How to Practice the Weekly Affirmations

All the affirmations are designed specifically to speed your recovery from having been defined as less than you are or not who you are.

Many people find it helpful to write an affirmation on a file or note card so they can post it where they will see it throughout the day. Like telling a joke you have just heard, repeating it can help you to remember it.

Also, your power to erase negative definitions will increase if, throughout the day, you repeat the affirmation to yourself. If you apply it to your day-to-day experience, positive thoughts will replace any negative thoughts and this in turn will lead to experiences that are more positive. If you miss a week or two, just start on the next affirmation without skipping any. If you notice that you have a negative thought that doesn't disappear with the affirmation of that week, say "erase!" and reverse it to a positive one. After you have begun with the first affirmation, this book can become part of your personal healing practice.

Sharing the affirmation with a friend or on Facebook or Twitter can help keep it in the forefront of your mind. If you do share online, please don't forget to cite the source of your favorite affirmation, *Victory over Verbal Abuse.*

The affirmations are not meant to replace any other avenues you may pursue to improve your life. They are designed, instead, to support you in your pursuits, whatever they may be. For example, you may be seeing a therapist, involved in a support group, seeking employment, changing careers, taking a dance class, cultivating friendships, taking up golf, or getting a degree in a field of your interest. You may be focused on raising your children, or discovering your own interests and talents. You may be involved in any combination of these or other goals. What's important is that you are resolved to make your life as healthy and happy as possible and to reverse any discouragement with a positive affirmation.

Here is an example of how a positive affirmation can support you. Please imagine that you've been very busy, handling many details and missed a payment on a credit card. You find, just a day later, that you have a late charge. If your negative thought is, "I can't do anything right. I always mess up," you may not think of calling the bank to reduce the fee, or if you do think of calling and your negative thought is, "They'll probably say no," you will probably make your payment including the late charge.

If, instead, you have a positive thought, and say, "I can handle this. I can probably get this late charge removed, because I've never been late before," you would likely call the bank, and when confronted with someone who tells you no, you may ask to talk to the supervisor and not wanting to lose your business the supervisor will likely remove the late charge. You not only save money, you have a success and feel more empowered. Even if the supervisor doesn't agree to your request, you can congratulate yourself on having done the best you could.

No matter what you are doing, or what goals you have set, an affirmation is there to enhance your success. I hope you will make the affirmations part of your personal healing practice and be part of dispelling the cloud of verbal abuse that has settled over much of our planet.

Your Notes

Following each affirmation and the message that accompanies it, there is an area for notes. If you make a brief note of how the affirmation worked for you, or of your goal at the time, you will have a reminder of where you were and what you were doing months or even years later. At the end of the week, when you write your note, ask yourself if the affirmation empowered you in some way? Did it remind you of some negative concept you were told about yourself, one that you now know to be ridiculous? Did it inspire you to confront a fear or a challenge that week? Did you simply feel more positive about your life or more optimistic about the future?

When you have completed all fifty-two affirmations, begin again. Then, take a look at what you wrote the previous year and use your note as a touchstone. You may be awed by how far you have come, all you've achieved and learned and how you've moved closer to your goals. Congratulate yourself, knowing where you were the year before, and charting your progress for years to come.

Week 1

Your Affirmation: I am self-defining.

Your Message The magic of being a unique human being is that only you can define yourself. If you recall some abusive comment that defines you, your motives, thoughts, or feelings, you may choose to laugh at the comment because you know that no one on earth knows your thoughts, feelings, needs, motives, or future. Only you can know what you are, want, feel, should do, how to do what you do, and so forth.

You might recall having heard something like, "You're trying to start a fight." You then might wonder, "How crazy is that? Someone was telling me my motives!" Then say "erase!" and focus on something else. If you were defined in any way, you heard nonsense, irrational comments, and pretend talk.

No one can take away your freedom to define yourself. Self-definition is the gift of consciousness. The moment you think of the abusive comment, focus on this affirmation because you truly are self-defining and so you will not entertain the comment for a moment longer.

If you happen to be in the presence of someone who negatively defines you, it is okay to laugh at his or her irrational behavior. Laughter is a human response to the mentally unexpected, even nonsensical statement. You may laugh and laugh at any nonsensical statement. But, laugh only if it is safe to do so and you know who is defining you.

Here is an example of how laughing works in some cases. A nine-year-old boy named Russ came back to school after summer vacation, and just before he went back, he was sunburned. His face was very red. Some boys tried to bully him by shouting at him, "Russ is Rusty, Russ is Rusty." It was so funny to him that he laughed so hard he couldn't stand up. He got over his laughter, caught his breath, noticed they were gone, and later noticed they never called him that again.

This week and in the weeks to come remind yourself that you are indeed self-defining.

My Notes: From Week 1

Week 2

Your Affirmation: I am part of all. I belong.

Your Message This affirmation is helpful especially if you feel adrift, unimportant, undeserving, or unworthy. If you notice that you are lonely, or find yourself thinking, "I'll always be alone," simply say to yourself "erase!" to get that negative thought out of your mind while you focus on this affirmation: "I am part of all. I belong."

Everyone has come from the first starburst, so you are connected to and a part of all humanity. You are also an individual. No one is exactly like you. No one can see the world exactly through your eyes. Knowing this, you not only know that no one can define you, but also that you are part of all. You are not alone. You take up space and time in this present moment and you can overcome all the indoctrination you have heard and even adapted to. You can overcome all the irrational comments that defined you.

When you express yourself creatively, you bring forth something new, be it music, dance, song, art, poetry, or anything else that was not here or not expressed this way before. Thus, you tap into the creative force. This "bringing forth" happens because you are connected to all. This may even explain simultaneous inventions—when, for instance, two people in two different places invent something at the same time without either knowing about the other. Since you are part of the universe, you are connected to all and are definitely not alone. You belong, just as much as any person on earth. At the same time, you are unique.

Another way to know that you are connected to all and not alone is through the experience of synchronicity. When you experience a synchronicity, your connection to all is validated.

Synchronicity is an unexplainable experience of two events occurring at the same time that have real meaning to the person so affected. The Swiss psychologist Carl G. Jung described and defined synchronicity in the 1920s. He also gave an example of a patient who told him of a dream in which she saw a golden scarab. As she was talking, an insect appeared outside of his cabinet and when he caught it, it proved to be a golden scarab. It was rarely seen, if at all in that area. Thus, there were two events (the dream and the scarab's appearance) occurring together in a meaningful manner. Since this was so unlikely, Jung ruled out coincidence.

My Notes: From Week 2

____

____

____

____

____

____

____

____

____

____

____

____

____

____

____

Week 3

Your Affirmation: The spirit of life at my center thrives in the shelter of my courage.

Your Message At times, it takes courage to act on your own behalf, to not give up, to do the difficult, to give a hundred percent in service of your values and needs. Even when it is difficult, having the courage to act on your own behalf will, in the long run, uplift your spirits.

For instance, it may seem difficult to have to ask for help, advice, encouragement, or to handle some task that you never had to do before, but finding the courage within yourself will build your courage to act on your own behalf in the future.

If you have been deprived of loving emotional support, you may try to handle whatever comes up all by yourself. It is okay to ask for support—it does not mean that you are not good enough to handle it on your own.

One of the ways to foster courage within yourself is to view your spirit and emotional self as precious, depending upon you for their health and well-being. What would you do for a person you love, a sister, mother, or friend? If you ask yourself this question, an answer will come to you.

When you draw upon your inner courage to act on your own behalf, you are giving yourself the opportunity to achieve success. Each success you do achieve will increase your courage to meet new challenges and will build your confidence and self-esteem—the self-esteem that verbal abuse attempts to erode.

My Notes: From Week 3

Week 4

Your Affirmation: I make good choices because I frequently review my priorities.

Your Message As you affirm to yourself that you do make good choices, you will be more inclined to make them—to be decisive. Knowing your priorities simplifies choosing. Here is a short checklist to use for important decisions:

- Am I making a life-changing decision while in trauma?
- Have I gathered all the information I need to make a good decision?
- What are my priorities?
- What is the highest good for me and also for others?
- What do I need versus what do I want?
- What are my values?
- What would be the best and the worst possible outcomes of my decision?
- Can I handle any outcome?
- Do I have a backup plan?

When it comes to a new relationship, if you find that the person you have come to know is not the person you thought he was, you have the power to make a choice to end it. Generally, if this is simply a dating relationship and you aren't living together, an e-mail or call would work. If this is a marriage with children, then it is advisable to seek professional advice and to go through the list above. If you have presented the perpetrator of abuse with a list of JPS behaviors and seen no real change and choose to end the relationship, you do not need the perpetrator's permission to do so.

You have no obligation to make a person who indulges in verbal abuse feel good about your ending the relationship, nor to try to change what an abuser may think about you, nor to worry about the abuser's feelings, nor to try to get the abuser to understand your point of view.

Every day brings new decisions. This week and during the weeks to come you are empowered to choose well because you know your priorities.

My Notes: From Week 4

Week 5

Your Affirmation: What is for my highest good is also good for all.

Your Message Your highest good is in keeping with truth, peace, and safety for all. Your intuition guides you. Also, your highest good is toward developing your own potentials, that is, becoming who you really are while also meeting your responsibilities. As you grow strong and overcome challenges, you are not only gaining the satisfaction such growth engenders, you are contributing your part to the world around you. Your highest good is good for all simply because you are a part of all. When you act to increase your own happiness over time and to gain the tranquility you desire, you are adding happiness and tranquility to the world.

Just as you know that you are not responsible for other people's abusive behaviors, you know that your real responsibility is to act on your own behalf for your highest good. Knowing this, you don't act impulsively but give due consideration to all aspects of your life.

In the long run, when you act in accordance with your highest good, you make the world a healthier place. How beautiful is that? Likewise, as you become increasingly aware of what works best for you, from the smallest thing like sleeping in and working late, to working at dawn and going to sleep early, to cultivating a new friendship, awareness directs your actions. The more aware you are, the more your inner direction will light your path to your highest good.

Your highest good is in keeping with truth, peace, commitments, personal safety, and the needs of any children in your care. Whenever you make a choice, you will consider the desired outcome that includes your happiness and tranquility.

While you aim for your highest good and tune in to your intuition, the unseen forces that compel all growth support you.

As you become more aware, you raise awareness for all because you are a part of all. This week and in weeks to come as you act for your highest good, you bring more goodness into the world.

My Notes: From Week 5

Week 6

Your Affirmation: I don't settle for what is only a little bit okay, but look for what I really want.

Your Message Having high self-esteem means that you value yourself and so know that you are worth the effort, hope, and determination it takes to take care of yourself. When making a decision, ask yourself, "Will this decision be in my best interests and will it serve me in the long run? Is this what I really want?"

With high self-esteem you will choose the best for yourself, be it the healthiest foods to the most trustworthy friends, just as you would choose for a child you love. No matter what you have been told about yourself, how badly you've been treated, and how much of your life you have endured abuse, you can be successful in building your own secure and loving environment.

Is there anything that you have put up with, not given yourself, not tried simply because you put yourself last? For instance, at a restaurant, have you received a wilted salad and not sent it back? Bought a bouquet for a friend but never for yourself? Put off looking for a class you would love to take? Stayed up later than you wanted and were too exhausted to function the next day because you didn't want to disappoint someone who wanted to stay out late? Heated your guest's tea, but drank yours barely warm? Didn't leave the premises when someone yelled at you because you didn't want to embarrass anyone?

Is there a choice you can make today for yourself? A vacation you need? A job you can apply for? Part of choosing is trying something out. Sometimes you may make a choice only to find that what you are trying out isn't what you really want. And so you have learned from this experience more about what works for you, what is okay and what is not. Much of life, maybe all of life, is this learning process. Settling for less than what you want is choosing not to have what you really do want.

This week and in weeks to come, I ask for what I need, choose what is best for me and don't settle for less. I'll take a chance on me.

My Notes: From Week 6

Week 7

Your Affirmation: I can say no to what I don't want and ask for what I do want, and this is getting easier every day.

Your Message Asking is simply opening up to one possibility and seeing if there is a yes or no response. Likewise, saying no to something asked of you or expected of you, is healthy if it doesn't work for you or puts too much pressure on you, or overwhelms you. It is so important that you know that it is okay to say no to what doesn't work for your highest good. So many times people who have been deprived of warmth and caring may feel that they must please everyone in order to be accepted. This is a sign of low self-esteem. This conditioning makes it very difficult to say no. In fact, people who unconsciously feel that they have to please others, feel guilty when they say no. Here are some ways that one can say "no" in a simple way:

- "I can't undertake that now"
- "No, that is not going to work for me"
- "No, I don't want to buy that now"

Knowing that your own highest good takes priority over other choices makes choosing for yourself easier. Asking is another matter. If, either in a relationship or in childhood, no one listened to you or no one understood what you needed, asking for what you want can be difficult. For instance, you might have come to someone with a problem who discounted it, or got angry or upset that you even had a problem. Here is an example that many people have experienced: A parent got angry with a child when the child complained about being bullied at school. This verbal abuse would surely leave the child conditioned neither to ask for assistance nor to express his or her wants and needs.

It is good to help others, but never at your own risk. For instance, if you take off work to help a friend move and are using your last sick day to do so, you risk having no sick leave when you really need it. If you are, or have been, in a relationship where you were told (when you haven't asked) what you "should" or "must" do, you may choose to use your personal power to say, "no," "nope," "no, thanks," or "I'm not willing." If you have tried to meet other people's expectations, you may have lost your energy both to say no to people who ask too much of you, as well as to ask for what you do want. Here are some everyday examples of asking for what you want:

At the store: "Will you take this back? When I opened it, it was spoiled, didn't fit, and was the wrong color." The store may or may not take the item back; in either case you will know you chose to act on your own behalf.

At work: "Will you consider giving me a raise for the extra work I've taken on?" "Will you consider covering these expenses since they help out the company?"

Choosing to ask for what you want is a wonderful way to grow your personal power. If you like, consider everyone you know and ask yourself if there is anything you need or want from any person. If there is, you may choose to ask just to exercise your personal power to act on your own behalf.

This week, and in the coming weeks, knowing you belong, are a part of all, and choose your highest good, you may choose to exercise your personal power by asking for what you want and saying no to what you don't want.

My Notes: From Week 7

Week 8

Your Affirmation: I seek counsel only with the wise and share only with those I trust.

Your Message You have the power of discernment, the power to apprehend the difference between those whom you can trust and those who are not to be trusted. Sometimes, however, a person may only *seem* wise and trustworthy but really isn't. This is the time to trust your intuition. Luckily, with this affirmation you are already giving direction to your intuition, and even to your unconsciousness, to guide you in your choice of friends and confidants. Titles and wealth do not prove a person trustworthy enough to advise you on investments. Memberships and affiliations do not prove a person is truly able to grasp your spiritual and emotional needs. Sharing insights with those who might jealously discount them puts your energy and spirit at risk.

Mark Twain said, "Keep away from those who try to belittle your ambitions. Small people always do that, but the really great make you believe that you too can become great."

Asking for help or understanding from someone who has disappointed you in the past will likely lead to more disappointment. Your determination to share only with those who have shown you that they are trustworthy and actually wise is fundamental to recovery.

Every day you are more aware. If you, for example, tell a friend about someone yelling at you or putting you down, and your friend makes comments like, "You're blowing it out of proportion," or, "Get over it," or "It takes two," you have had a conversation with someone who is not wise or conscious. You can choose to protect yourself in the future with your personal power to choose for your highest good. You may choose to distance yourself from anyone who discounts your experience. And, just as importantly, you may choose to refuse to give any credence to such abusive comments. This week and during the weeks to come, your trust in your own wisdom and experience will serve you well.

My Notes: From Week 8

Week 9

Your Affirmation: I have the strength, confidence, and courage to pursue my goals.

Your Message Sharing your goals and progress with a friend, family member, personal coach, or group may further empower you to reach them. You may also choose to empower yourself by keeping a journal of your progress and the steps that you take to achieve them. You may find it useful to make two lists, one of your long-term goals and one of your short-term goals. While you may occasionally revise your long-term goals, your short-term goals may be more like a to-do list for the coming days or weeks. If you keep your lists on your computer, they will be easy to update. If you move completed goals to the bottom of the page, you will see your progress right before your eyes.

Updating your goals journal, seeing the results, accomplishing your goals, completing the steps needed to enhance the quality of your life can inspire and amaze you. With strength, confidence and courage, whatever your means or circumstances, you may choose to treat yourself kindly and draw on your courage to never give up on yourself.

Many people find that making a vision board of what they want brings surprisingly quick results. The board is filled with pictures that symbolize their goals and includes their hopes and wishes. It is a collage of pictures often cut from old magazines and pasted on a poster board. The images impact them without their conscious notice, in such a way, they say, that what they desire comes to them much more quickly than they ever expected. Each picture is a symbol that works from behind the scenes, so to speak.

Some examples of what might be used to make a board are:

- Desire to travel—a plane and luggage
- A great class to teach—a classroom of happy, smiling children
- A raise in salary—a pile of money

This week, if you choose to begin your goals list and visualization board, you may be awed by how inspired, strengthened, and ever more confident you become. In the weeks to come, you may be even more amazed at all your increasing confidence and courage.

My Notes: From Week 9

____

____

____

____

____

____

____

____

____

____

____

____

____

____

____

Week 10

Your Affirmation: I develop my talents and use them to gain my greatest satisfaction.

Your Message Whenever you accomplish anything, whether it's putting in a day's work or remembering to replace negative thoughts with positive ones, congratulations are in order. "I did a good job," or "I did something good for myself today." If you don't already allow yourself to really experience satisfaction, now is a great time to begin.

One of the easiest ways to experience satisfaction is to use your talents. You are designed to express them. In fact, your talents reveal your place in the world. You may have an ability to handle detail or relate to children, a flare for languages, artistic or musical talent.

You are meant to flourish, just as each of the hundreds of thousands of plants and trees in the world each become what they were meant to be. And, just as a desert plant doesn't try to be a tropical forest plant, you grow to be the person you were meant to be. If there is something you are good at, or that you love to do, then that ability or inclination reveals a talent, definitely one of many.

You may discover hidden talents in many ways, including tests, evaluations, and by simply pursuing what you like most. For instance, if you love art, or music, or languages, consider pursuing a career or avocation or education to add even more meaning and purpose to your life. You are empowered to stay positive. Your life reveals your gifts and talents as you use them over time. What is your passion?

This week and in weeks to come, you may see signs of your talents. A sign may come to you in a dream, in a desire to try something new, or in even the slightest inclination to do something.

My Notes: From Week 10

Week 11

Your Affirmation: I bring balance into the structure of my days.

Your Message Have you done something for fun now and then, accomplished something at work or toward getting the job or career you really want, reached a goal, meditated a little, relaxed, exercised, eaten foods that are good for you, had some time to visit with a friend?

Since you are positive about bringing balance into your days, if there is any area that is out of balance, you may choose to do what you can to spend more time doing what will benefit you in the long run. Enhancing areas of your life that may have been neglected will energize other areas.

When an artist attends the theater and sees an avant-garde play, she may be inspired to create a new painting. Creativity inspires creativity. An exercise group inspires one to keep exercising and so on. It is easier to bring balance to your days if you are with like-minded people who share your interests and goals. It is easier to take even the smallest step than to wish you had taken that step. You are worth everything you can do for yourself. And you are meant to grow all your life in a balanced and beautiful way.

While not expecting any kind of perfection in doing all you hope to do, focusing on this affirmation all week will bring benefits that can inspire you to create an ever more satisfying life this week and for weeks to come.

My Notes: From Week 11

Week 12

Your Affirmation: I trust my intuition. It is always with me.

Your Message How blessed and honored humanity is that intuition is one of our four functions. Intuition comes from beyond our ability to figure things out, to see and hear with our normal senses. Intuition speaks with the language of one's soul or spirit. If you aren't already tuning in to your intuition and letting it guide you, there are some simple ways to begin. If you already do rely on your intuition, here are some ways to develop awareness of it.

Most important is that you trust your intuition especially if you ever have a strong sense that some person or some place holds some danger. Sometimes your intuition sends a very strong message by way of a feeling. If you have a sudden feeling of real fear as you are about to do something—step in an elevator, enter your home, or meet with someone—don't proceed. Your intuition could save your life.

You can access your intuition by asking yourself, "What is my intuition telling me about this?" Be still and listen to that inner voice or note your felt sense of the situation. Whenever you need a hunch about something, ask yourself, what is my intuition telling me? For example, you can't find your keys. Relax, sit back, and ask, "Are my keys lost?" If you get no sinking feeling or visceral response in your body, the keys are probably misplaced. If you think something like, "I'll never find them," you may feel upset and this may indicate a conflict between your intuition and your thinking. Your intuition guides you if you practice tuning in to it. Here is another way to access your intuition. If you think, "I can't find my pen," and you don't feel a real sense of loss, this is likely your intuition telling you that you misplaced it and it will be found.

As your intuition informs you, it becomes increasingly your own guidance system, and your trust in yourself increases. Another way your intuition works is when it informs you that you did the right thing. For example, you make an important decision to take a particular job when you have two options, or you decide on a college course that will take you in a new direction, and then you suddenly feel absolute peace and serenity. It is as if your intuition is saying, "Yes, yes, yes."

This week, remind yourself, "I trust my intuition in all things." Then, when you have to make a decision, check in with your intuition. If your intuition is telling you to call someone, to check in on someone, don't hesitate to act on your intuition.

Sometimes your intuition may give you a message in a dream. If you have a dream that is different from your normal dreams, and if there is a clear message in it, that also is your intuition speaking. A woman shared this story about an intuitive dream. And with her permission, I share this example of intuition working in a dream. She said, "In the dream it was 10 A.M. I saw the clock and heard the phone ring, I picked it up and heard my daughter, who was away at college, say, 'Mom, I feel so bad.' [After I woke up] I didn't have time to think about it as I got into my morning to-dos and then at 10:00 A.M. on the dot, my phone rang. I picked it up and heard my daughter's voice say, 'Mom, I feel so bad.' I was shocked; it was the same as my dream. It had not been a lasting crisis for her. It was soon healed, but she did feel badly at the time. I wished I had called her right after the dream."

Throughout the week and in weeks to come, as you remind yourself that your intuition is always with you, I am confident that you will experience it working for you throughout your days.

My Notes: From Week 12

Week 13

Your Affirmation: I face each new day like it was the first day of the rest of my life.

Your Message Even as old memories and routines surface, you may choose to think of this brand new day as the first day of your life. If you think of this day as the beginning of your new life, you may do something, try something, and experience something you never experienced before. You may discover something new about yourself that you didn't know was within you. You may read a poem, meditate on the stillness of a tree, try an ethnic dish you've never tasted, have a cup of coffee or tea in a shop you've never visited, sign up for a dance, watercolor, or yoga class, take time to meet a new neighbor.

As you relax now and think of this day as the first day of the rest of your life, close your eyes and ask yourself, what new experience would you like to have. See what comes to you. Even ask your emotional self, the little one you met in the process in Chapter 5 of this book, what new experience would she like to have on this, the first day of the rest of her life. It may not be something that can be done this day, or possibly not even this year, but there is one thing at least that can be done to bring it to fruition. If it takes money, a dime or more in a jar starts the process. If it takes an education, ten minutes on a computer researching classes and colleges can start the process. Whatever it takes, there is a beginning.

It is good to do this each morning of the week and see what you get. If nothing comes to you one day, simply stay aware and notice if you feel inclined to do something. It could be as simple as feeling the silkiness of a leaf you never touched before, or tuning into some music you've not listened to before. Your life is new each day and you write your own story. This week and in weeks to come view each day as a new page in the story of your life and you will be both the writer and the reader creating your own adventure through the actions and choices you make.

My Notes: From Week 13

Week 14

Your Affirmation: My tears water my spirit, my truth feeds it, and so it revives.

Your Message Tears may come from loss, pain, and feelings of powerlessness, futility, frustration, and even exhaustion. They may also come from an overwhelming feeling of joy or love that touches you in a moving moment. In all cases, they are healing as they release something that has no other way out. In the case of grief over a loss, be it the loss of a relationship, a child, a friend, a parent, a lifestyle, or home, whatever the loss, it can be healed, and your spirit, revived through your grieving, will grow stronger.

Affirming to yourself what you know to be true will also revive your spirit. As you think about what is true about you, for instance, that you are not abusive and have always tried to do what is right, think about what is true of your circumstances. Are you living within your means? Are the people around you emotionally healthy or toxic to you? All truth is important to your healing.

Many people have heard, "Where there's a will, there's a way." A woman said, "Although I may feel like a boxer who just was knocked down in the ring, though it be emotionally, I still can get back on my feet, brush myself off, and try again, refusing to stop until I reach my goal."

Holding strongly to your truth, letting go of other people's definitions of you, will also revive your spirit. If, for example, someone told you, "You'll never be able to . . ." or "You can't . . ." or "You should . . . ," let their words dissolve as silly talk. Hold to your truth and know that no one can tell you these things. Your spirit will thrive and energize you as you hold to your own truth.

Carl Jung, known as one of the world's most influential psychiatrists, described grieving your losses as essential to healing. One of his famous quotes is, "Even a happy life cannot be without a measure of darkness, and the word 'happy' would lose its meaning if it were not balanced by sadness."

A woman said, "I know better than to do what others say when I feel in my soul I know a better way, just like I know right from wrong. I can be my own hero. I can forgive, even when forgiving means I have to go my own way, even if it means mourning loss."

This week and in weeks to come, acknowledge all your feelings with love and understanding.

My Notes: From Week 14

____

____

____

____

____

____

____

____

____

____

____

____

____

____

Week 15

Your Affirmation: I let go of the past and trust in the future.

Your Message The past does not predict the future. You can trust in the future as you use your time today, and each day, as wisely as you know how. The past, of course, cannot be changed; however, your experience of the past can change. Not only can it fade away, be erased and forgotten, but if remembered, words that hurt can be seen as something silly, irrational, and ignorant—as twitters from a twittering mind, meaningless as messages from a gumball machine, odd as jabbering from a padded cell. So easy to let go of that.

Any feeling from the past that you are not important or that you won't have a great future, could come from an imprint in your mind, for instance that you weren't good enough, or important enough, or that all your pain is your fault. One of the most powerful imprints a woman might have originates in cultures as well as religions and families. It is this. If you act on your own without approval from a man, you will suffer some terrible fate. To act on your own would be like breaking a taboo.

This imprint generates a feeling of dread. A woman so afflicted may feel dread if she does anything on her own behalf that isn't already approved of by her significant other. She feels like she is breaking a taboo, but doesn't know where the feeling of dread comes from. As she begins acting on her own behalf and understands where the feeling originates, it dissipates. After all, she knows that it is simply a rule made up to oppress. Letting go of the past includes recognizing oppressive feelings and understanding that the healing journey is a heroic one.

A woman wrote, "As I float past every skeptic, suddenly I grow wings, and I become the one that excites admiring awe in myself."

During this week and in weeks to come, ask what you can do for your greater peace, harmony and well-being each day to make your future better. Congratulate yourself on the wisdom you have gained from all your experiences and be confident that your newly found wisdom will serve you well.

My Notes: From Week 15

Week 16

Your Affirmation: The universe is true so when I am aligned with truth the universe supports me.

Your Message Wow! Since the universe is true and some say God is truth, then there is a great support system within you. Some say it is your soul, your spirit, your conscience, your intuition, or your instincts. Whenever you seek the truth, act on truth, tell the truth, or stand up for the truth, you are aligned with the universe.

This week, resolve to focus on what you know to be true. If anyone defined you, told you who you are, what you want, think, or feel, they were lying to you. You don't have to prove they were wrong. In fact, trying to prove they were wrong, or trying to convince them they were wrong about you, diverts all your energy away from your own development, from rediscovering what is true about you. That is what counts. You count.

When you tell someone to stop defining you, you act from truth. When you protect your children, you act from truth. When you leave an abuser who refuses to change, you act from truth. When you are too traumatized to stay, and so leave an abuser, you act on truth. When you are with a person who is doing everything possible to change and wait to see because you want to, you act on truth.

When you act on your truth, the universe supports you in such a way that sometimes obstacles are later seen as stepping-stones. You may choose to make your truth the knowledge that the universe supports you not only this week but in all the weeks to come.

My Notes: From Week 16

Week 17

Your Affirmation: I cultivate friendships with people who share my interests and views.

Your Message Developing nurturing friendships is not always easy. Many people who have been in relationships that define them have also been isolated from former friends and even family. This week you might begin developing your support system, friends you can count on even if they don't know about or understand what you've been through. With the past behind you, look for people who have healthy behavior. Do everything you can to avoid isolation. Use the Internet to see what organizations, groups, associations, or classes are in your area and match your interests. As you meet people, stay alert and aware of anyone who attempts to define you or others. Then limit contact with those who make you feel uncomfortable.

Friendships are cultivated over time and as you look back in time at those who have been there for you, you know they share history with you. Many people find that even if they only meet with a friend occasionally, their memories come back so when they do meet it seems as though no time has passed. Friends provide the emotional support we expect from families, but for some, friends are more like family than their own relatives. Friendships fill our lives with life. If you have been isolated or have had to start your life over in a new way, you may choose to make new friends. Work and social situations, clubs, classes, interest groups are all areas where new friends can be found and the Internet is a handy resource for finding like-minded people. Your friends will be there for you as you are for them as you reach out to others this week and in weeks to come.

My Notes: From Week 17

Week 18

Your Affirmation: The universe supports me in self-discovery and success.

Your Message The universe is a driving force in support of your self-discovery and success. Every single person in the world is unique and is born with her own unique combination of attributes, inclinations, and gifts. Just as a desert and a lake each support different flowers, from water lilies to elegant flowering cacti, each person is meant to develop her own potentials, to unfold and flower into who she is.

One would not know that a seed was meant to be a great tree, nor another seed was meant to be an aromatic mint until it sprouts and begins to grow. One only sees it as it becomes what it was meant to be. The seed, like the newborn infant holds its own unique potentials.

As you follow your inclinations, develop your talents, and meet your needs, your life becomes a process of discovery and greater satisfaction. Thus, you see more of yourself. You grow in consciousness. From this perspective, life is an exciting adventure and the universe not only supports you in your becoming, just as it does a seed, but the universe itself is always becoming.

Once in a while people may discover something about themselves, such as a talent that they never dreamt they had. It may be so unexpected that the person is said to have a not-me experience. It might be something like what happened to a person answering all 200 questions correctly on a class survey test on a subject that she had no knowledge about. In this case, the professor gave the ungraded test only to see what the students might know prior to teaching the subject. Since only a few students each year even got about 65 percent right, the professor announced the 100 percent score to the class and named the student. It was a first for the professor but also a first for the student. She was so shocked she felt a strange anxiety float through her. This might be described as the feeling of "I am not the me that I know."

Whether she had phenomenal intuition, had remembered a past life, could mentally time travel or had unbelievable luck did not matter to her. What did matter was incorporating the experience into her identity, "I am a person who knows something that I never knew I knew. I have some kind of gift."

The important thing to know is that self-discovery makes life an exciting adventure.

During this coming week, view every day as an opportunity to discover your unique self and to support your own growth.

My Notes: From Week 18

____

____

____

____

____

____

____

____

____

____

____

____

Week 19

Your Affirmation: The universe supports me in my stand against injustice.

Your Message Verbal abuse undermines justice because it attempts to erase consciousness. It is like a sledgehammer slammed against awareness. Since a person who defines you is saying something both irrational and invasive that attempts to erase your consciousness, verbal abuse can be a grave injustice.

However, when you take a stand against verbal abuse, such as by saying, "That's nonsense," or "Stop!" you are supported by the greatest consciousness that exists. You are supported by the source of consciousness that is set up to bring each person to greater awareness. This is, so to speak, the goal of the universe, the goal of existence. Consequently, the person who lies to you, defines you, or defines others is acting against the flow of the universe.

Even if during this week and the weeks to come, you do not encounter anyone who defines you, you may remember some defining statement. You may have heard defining words long ago that remain in the background of your mind, a comment you internalized. If you notice that you are saying something to yourself like, "I should be over this by now," or "There must be something wrong with me," you may choose to take a stand against injustice by simply saying to yourself, "What I've been thinking is not true. People may say, 'Get over it,' but they cannot tell me what I should do. They aren't me! I'm doing remarkably well considering all I've been through."

When you refuse to believe how others define you, and instead listen to what you yourself know is true, you are standing against injustice. When you stand against injustice and stand *for* justice you are aligned with the universe! Your stand against verbal abuse aligns you with the goal of existence. One might say, "The force is with you." When you refuse, as well, to accept the defining of another, such as through stereotypes or prejudices, or the negative defining of a child, and instead speak up, you are also standing against injustice. Throughout this week and during weeks to come as you take a stand against verbal abuse, you are gaining strength, clarity, and alignment with the flow of the universe.

My Notes: From Week 19

Week 20

Your Affirmation: I trust in the abundance of the universe and I trust myself to do all I can to bring me what I need.

Your Message As you heal from the loss, pain, and self-doubt that verbal abuse creates, your understanding of just what happened to you becomes clear. With greater clarity, your confidence in yourself is strengthened. The effect of verbal abuse is lessened. If, for instance, you were told that you were wrong, or didn't know what you were talking about, or that you were too sensitive, in no way do these statements mean that you are, or were, any of these things.

In fact, verbal abuse defines you as the opposite of who you are. You can, therefore, trust yourself and know that if you do everything you can to heal, pursue the avenues open to you, and know that you can manifest abundance, you will be able to give yourself a safe, secure, and fulfilling life.

While it may take some time to trust others, you can trust yourself, especially if you resolve daily to act on your own behalf. As you experience guiding dreams and moments of inspiration, I am confident that you will increasingly recognize that you are interconnected with all and not alone.

Although some of your current circumstances may not reveal the abundance of the universe, your actions to gain the abundance you seek will not only provide you with more than you likely imagined, but will also reveal your strengths, talents, inner resources and gifts. All these experiences will enhance your trust in yourself. As you bring your inner resources to bear upon your goals, your intelligence, research, intuition, intentions, creativity, and faith in yourself will be revealed to you.

It is as if the abundance of the universe, and your actions to bring that abundance into your life, work together to bring about your greatest fulfillment.

Your trust in yourself and your determination to never give up on yourself will serve you throughout this week and in the weeks to come.

My Notes: From Week 20

Week 21

Your Affirmation: My intentions are aligned with my greatest good and are based on my values.

Your Message You may choose to make a list of your values to clarify your intentions. Some kinds of values are social, ethical, spiritual, moral, cultural, and esthetic. Here are a few examples: a social value may be peace, an ethical value may be integrity, a spiritual value might be love, a moral value might be honesty, a cultural value might be honor of elders, an esthetic value might be beauty. Internet searches offer various lists of values that may inspire you to create your own list if you choose. You might simply ask yourself what you value and see what comes to mind.

Here is a sample: when I ask myself, "What do I value?" honesty, family, peace, integrity, order, balance, and freedom come to mind. They are in no particular order, but like the numbers on a clock equidistant from the center, where I reside.

Whatever your values are, your intentions are aligned with them when you consciously act upon them and use them as a basis for your decisions: for example, to speak honestly, to enjoy family, to encourage peacefulness, to keep your commitments and promises.

With your intentions and actions aligned you may feel assured that you are doing your best with integrity, that you honor your process, even the difficult times, and will never accept any negative definition of who you are. And best of all, you can count on the fact that you are consistently acting on your own behalf toward your greatest good. This week and in weeks to come, your self-esteem increases from simply knowing that you've done your best to act according to your good intentions.

My Notes: From Week 21

Week 22

Your Affirmation: I am confident even as I confront the unknown.

Your Message If you know your values and hold true to them in all you do, you can act in your best interest even when facing an unknown situation or uncertain future. Hold true to yourself and you will be able to handle the unknown.

New situations and challenges arise frequently as people pursue their interests, their careers, and their personal development, all in a world that is changing. Since you appreciate yourself and accept yourself, you can choose to be confident that the real you is able to handle anything new, for instance, living on your own after a divorce or starting a new job. Likewise, your confidence will grow as you make decisions based on any information you gather and what your intuition tells you.

Resolve to trust yourself to make decisions on your own behalf. Whether you are about to confront the unknown of a new residence or virtually a new life, you will be prepared to face any unknown situation. Choose to remind yourself that you can handle whatever comes up because you are bringing all of yourself to the new situation. You can be confident that your creative, resourceful, empowered self will handle whatever comes up with integrity and confidence.

Confidence comes from mastery and is gained over time. If you break down any problem into the smallest steps toward its solution, your confidence will grow as you master each step. Each success will then add to your confidence. As your confidence grows it is easier to remember to talk to yourself in a positive way. When facing the unknown it is essential that you do so. If you grew up hearing positive statements from your parents, it is much easier to encourage yourself as your parents encouraged you. If you did not receive that kind of encouragement, it may take a little practice.

Common statements many people hear as children are, "Where there's a will, there's a way," or "You can do it." Some ways to encourage yourself are:

- "Whatever comes up, I can handle it."
- "A step into the unknown is like an adventure."
- "I stay focused in the present and tomorrow will take care of itself."

Even as people plan their futures something unknown and unanticipated confronts them every day. It may be big or small, but no one is exempt from the unknown.

This week and in the weeks to come you may choose to live with confidence and encouragement.

My Notes: From Week 22

____

____

____

____

____

____

____

____

____

Week 23

Your Affirmation: Mastery of anything new increases my self-esteem and confidence.

Your Message Mastery and success build confidence. Ask yourself if there is any skill or any knowledge that you would like to acquire. Now may be the time to discover if there is a way to acquire it. You can start small; even one step can show you what is possible. In fact, small steps really can bring you mastery. For example, if you have always wanted to master a foreign language, thinking of how much there would be to learn can be overwhelming and stop you before you start. However, doing a little research on books, courses, and other materials would be a first step. Once you have selected what you will use, break up the work into small steps.

Never doubt that you can achieve your goals successfully and master anything from a foreign language to a computer application to a new job, if you take easy small steps. Just as children build self-esteem through mastery from learning to tie their own shoes to depositing a birthday check in their own bank account, as you master new skills, achieve your goals, and have new experiences, your self-esteem will increase in a healthy way.

If you have ever doubted yourself after hearing negative statements you can be confident that you are not in any way like you were told you were, in fact you are just the opposite.

When facing an unknown situation or unknown future, hold true to yourself and you will be able to handle the unknown. Be assured that your success each day will increase your self-esteem and confidence. A woman said, "I have it in me, even though I may not think I do, to do anything in this world I want to. I know I just have to want to bad enough."

Tell yourself, "This week and in weeks to come my confidence and self-esteem grow in harmony with my accomplishments."

My Notes: From Week 23

Week 24

Your Affirmation: I praise and value myself and honor my successes.

Your Message Enjoy and value your successes. Your path may not always be smooth and may have some setbacks but focus on what is right; where you have succeeded, praise yourself and know that you will be able to continue moving forward in your healing, recovery, and self-discovery. A woman once described some of the fears, losses, and physical setbacks she had been through. The small group around her felt empathy for her and wondered how anyone should have had to endure the setbacks she had faced. Then she said it was, indeed, difficult to overcome all this, but she said, "I honor the process of going through it all."

She saw overcoming adversity as a success. If you, too, can consider your survival a success, then surely you can see that the goals you've met, those you've set, and all that you have learned are all part of your success. All your hard-won achievements are gained because deep within you is the valuable self you are meant to care for. This week and for weeks to come, please know that your success will serve you every day and will be an inspiration to others.

My Notes: From Week 24

Week 25

Your Affirmation: I choose for myself, not against myself, in my thoughts and actions.

Your Message Your thoughts and choices reflect who you are and how you want to grow. Stay tuned in to what you think about yourself and what you say to yourself. If you have a thought like, "I'm not good at ________________," or "They probably think I'm stupid," or "I'll never get over this," you have chosen against yourself. Change your thoughts when you notice them and watch your life change.

When it comes to your actions, thinking a bit about your choices before you decide works well. "I'll sleep on it," or "I'll get back to you on it," are handy tools available to give yourself time. Then choose what will move you along the path you desire.

As your life choices bring you ever-increasing satisfaction and self-esteem, you may choose to actively look at your hidden talents, gifts and energies. Here are some suggestions.

- *Notice what seems to come easy to you.* If you carry a tune, then you might define yourself as having some musical talent. If you find it easy to organize paperwork or data that must be organized, then you might define yourself as a good organizer.
- *Notice what is most satisfying to you.* Do you enjoy helping a child to read, finding the solution to a crossword puzzle, traveling, learning new things?
- *Look at what you are passionate about.* If you don't know what it is, and don't feel passionate about anything, give yourself some time and try out some new things where you may have had an inclination in the past.

- *Take some tests.* If the feedback you received from a parent or couple relationship was that you are not smart or aren't going to amount to anything, take an IQ test, an interests test, or a personality assessment test, or all of these.
- *Check out your natal horoscope.* This isn't about your predicting the future but about discovering your basic energies and in what area you might be gifted. See if it makes sense to you. Skip it if it doesn't. Online sites can give you your natal chart at no cost, or you can purchase a computer program that will tell you what planets were in what signs at the time of your birth and in what houses they play out their energy. They usually show positive and negative qualities, which correspond to conscious/aware versus unconscious/negative potentials and qualities. Since you are actively pursuing consciousness and may be in recovery from negativity, I suggest that you only review the positive side.

This week and in weeks to come, choose for yourself every time.

My Notes: From Week 25

____

____

____

____

____

____

____

____

____

Week 26

Your Affirmation: I praise myself as I look back on all I've accomplished.

Your Message Everyone has accomplished many things in their lives. Acknowledging your accomplishments can help you discover and uncover your strengths and talents. Also, everyone has setbacks or bad moments, but remembering and praising yourself for all you have accomplished can help get you back on track.

If you see any challenges that come along this week through the lens of your achievements, they will be easier to manage. While some readers may recall getting a raise, or an award, or onto a team, or into a college as their memorable achievement, others may consider a less tangible achievement as their most memorable. For instance, they may consider overcoming a fear, facing uncertainty with fortitude, escaping from a destructive relationship, or overcoming a depression highly notable.

You may choose to congratulate yourself on an accomplishment. You might make a list of your accomplishments, and then say to yourself, "If I could handle that, I can handle any challenge that comes up today or tomorrow, and ever after."

A reader expressed how she would see her future accomplishments, "Leaving abuse behind, I'll reach so high that I'll marvel at who I've become. I will gaze with wonder staring in astonishment at me, and who I've become. And I will leave any abuser only one thing, my memory!"

This week and for weeks to come, can you look with wonder at all you have done and declare yourself awesome?

My Notes: From Week 26

Week 27

Your Affirmation: Whenever I try new things, I pay attention to my experience and I learn more about what I like and don't like.

Your Message Each new experience, whether you are in a relationship or trying a new food or hobby, is your opportunity to learn and to grow. Do not regret a choice or think, "I wish I had/hadn't. . ." but think instead, "Next time I will/won't . . ." and use this as a learning experience. If you see all new experiences as learning experiences, then all are successful.

Life is a series of events, paths taken, changes in direction, gains and losses, and all are learning experiences. Why? Because life itself is about self-discovery. When you discover something that you enjoy, you can then define yourself as a person who likes "that." If, additionally, you learn some skill, or how to do something, you can define yourself as a person who likes "that" and can do "this."

Sometimes it takes a little extra willpower to do something new because feeling comes after doing. For instance, when you do something good for yourself, then you feel better. Do you recall times when you tried something new or gave yourself that little extra push to go do it? And do you remember that when you did it, you were glad that you did? You can choose to give yourself that little push to do something special for yourself, even if only to take a walk or take a course just because you feel better when you do.

During this week and in weeks to come be aware of your experience and see what gives you a good feeling. You may choose during this week and in weeks to come to do more and more of what makes you feel good.

My Notes: From Week 27

Week 28

Your Affirmation: The creative power of the universe supports me in discovering and using my gifts and talents because my gifts and talents come from the creative source.

Your Message When you do something that gives you joy, you are being true to yourself. Think of the times you have felt joy and seek out more of those experiences. Perhaps it was when writing a poem, sketching a tree, holding a newborn baby, or planting a garden. Look for inspiration. Tune in to your intuition and know that your self-discovery is how you actually become part of the creative power of the universe. It would have no expression without that which expresses it. You are, therefore, a part of its expression. You have a place in the universe because you are here.

If you aren't at all sure who you really are, what you like, or what your talents, gifts, and interests really are, the creative power of the universe will move you toward your self-discovery at great speed. Your intention to discover yourself, and your willingness to take steps to discover what brings you joy are all that are needed.

This week and during the weeks to come, as you stay aware of your inclinations and seize on every opportunity to learn more about yourself, you will have begun a life of self-discovery. Your satisfaction and excitement about life will grow with you.

My Notes: From Week 28

Week 29

Your Affirmation: As I act on my own behalf and stay on my path doors will open where I never expected.

Your Message You may choose to hold your thoughts in the arms of optimism. And, where there is a void, it will be filled because that is the way of the universe. As you stay on your path, opportunities and synchronicities will appear like wildflowers springing up where you least expect them.

Occasionally there will be an amazing correspondence between what you are thinking about and its appearance in your life. It could be as simple as thinking how nice it would look to have a bowl of daisies on the kitchen counter, when a neighbor stops by with a bunch of daisies just for you. "I had too many daisies and thought you might like some," she says. Or as complex as describing last night's dream of a red and yellow bird to a friend when a small red and yellow bird lands on your window ledge—one unknown in your area. These synchronistic events are like encouragements that you are on your path and that you will have opportunities for success.

Your path is about your growing in awareness, confidence and purpose. The force that supports you is the same powerful force that supports all of nature growing into what it was meant to be. Because you have free will, knowing this and accepting it allows that force to empower you all this week and for all weeks to come. If you are dealing with changes in a relationship, your employment, your finances or anything else, you may feel alone and overwhelmed. This is the time to talk to your emotional self as described in Chapter 5. Then follow through on what you learn from the energizing response you receive through the archetypal energy of the great good father.

As you act on your own behalf trust that good things will come to you. If you don't know what to do next, then do what's up at the moment. It is as easy to expect the best as to expect the worst. If you have been watching for synchronicity in your life, and note such occasions, you will know that you are not alone. If you expect the best, and take every action you know to bring about the best for yourself, doors will open where you never expected. An interesting journal you might choose to start is that of unexpected good things that happen in your life. This week and for weeks to come, act on your own behalf and watch for doors to open for you.

My Notes: From Week 29

Week 30

Your Affirmation: When I recognize verbal abuse, I recognize toxic people and protect myself by staying away from them.

Your Message Observe the world and those around you. Notice when you are defined and recognize it as what someone else says about you and not what you really are. Since you care for yourself and protect yourself as a child of God, your determination to avoid toxic people is empowered by your love for a child of God. You can do no less than remove yourself from anyone who is toxic to you, just as you would take any child away from a raging fire.

Just as you remove your mind from thoughts of how anyone defined you, and stay away from toxic people, you might choose to validate the reality of any other person you see being defined. And just as you protect yourself from toxic people by avoiding them, you may also avoid the influence of those who speak against others in all the media that so surrounds us in this world. It is one thing for instance, for a politician to point out a vote that s/he doesn't agree with; it is another thing to define the motives and intentions of someone with no evidence.

During this week and in weeks to come you can not only choose to separate yourself from toxic people, but also to avoid falling under their influence.

My Notes: From Week 30

Week 31

Your Affirmation: I respond to all abuse by speaking up appropriately.

Your Message Verbal abuse is always about the abuser, not about you. When verbal abuse is directed to you, or to someone in your sphere, you can find the right words and demeanor to respond by remembering that their words and behavior stem from deep within *them*. Their words and behavior are not a true reflection of anyone else's worth, value, or true spirit. Knowing this, you are able to calmly address the perpetrator as though speaking to a destructive child.

Some of the qualities you can emulate are: a calm pond, undisturbed on the surface, with great power, life, and force beneath; a great redwood tree, alive for centuries, facing down a snowstorm; a female grizzly with a growl that demands the cub not venture past the boundaries. By remembering an empowering image just before you speak, you are powerful and you change the dynamics of the situation. The environment will respond to you, the way great lakes can change the land, the way old redwood trees draw energy and give it back, and the way the cub instantly responds to the right growl from the she-bear.

Even as you visualize your calm strength at any time you encounter abuse, you may also choose to visualize an empowering image when you are alone in a quiet moment just for practice. If you do, it is helpful to truly view the abuser's irrationality as a pathetic shortcoming. The abuser cannot respond to a rational explanation or expression of how you feel. The abuser may respond to a calm and clear statement such as one would make to a child. Here are some examples:

1. The calm pond works well with this one: "Now that's enough of that nonsense. This is a safe house and we won't have any name-calling/accusing/etc. here."
2. The redwood tree works well with this one: "I can't hear you unless you use your happy voice."
3. The protective bear works well with this one: "Hold it!" (Then to the child): "That was mean nonsense. You aren't hopeless/a baby/a wimp/whatever. You're a person and I love you just the way you are."

This week and in weeks to come, you will become ever more able to respond appropriately to verbal abuse whenever and wherever you hear it.

My Notes: From Week 31

____

____

____

____

____

____

____

____

____

____

____

____

____

Week 32

Your Affirmation: I leave any place where I don't feel comfortable.

Your Message It is liberating to know and to remind yourself that you are a free, separate, unique human being. By visualizing yourself as an adventurer on the path of life, you can not only choose to leave any situation where you don't feel comfortable, but also you can choose to see yourself doing just that. Your imagination is a great ally. If you are going to some event around some people you know, but are not sure if you will want to stay, you may imagine various ways you might leave.

"Oh," you might say as you check the time, "I have to go. I have something to do. Thanks so much." Always polite and respectful, you can still be your own person. You may exercise your freedom to leave any situation where you don't feel comfortable.

If in the presence of someone who is yelling at you, you can leave, simply saying, "I can't take the yelling." If you are in a relationship or foresee the possibility of any situation where you might need to leave, be prepared to do so. Have cash with you, a cell phone, some prearranged destinations in mind, and anything you might need for the time away. If you have children have a plan that includes their care.

You do not need permission from anyone to take care of yourself. No doom will befall you for acting on your own. It takes courage to act on your own when a controller may view your action as opposition. However, if there is a possibility of physical violence, if you are in a home where there are guns, if your intuition tells you that you are in danger, seek help and act cautiously.

My Notes: From Week 32

Week 33

Your Affirmation: Nothing can stop me from acting to improve my situation and my life.

Your Message Some improvements may take a long time, others may happen quickly, but never lose sight of your goals. Don't let others stand in your way by telling you that you aren't smart enough or don't have what it takes, and don't believe anyone's definitions of your friends, family, or interests.

Here is an example. A financially independent woman, separated from her spouse, mentioned to him that she was coming to my workshop. Amazingly, he said in a disparaging way, "So, you're going off to a cult." He spoke as if he were God and "knew" that the attendees were members of a cult. The irony is they were attending the workshop in order to escape the influence of someone's control over them, possibly as she was trying to escape his control over her. He implied that she and other attendees were doing the opposite.

He used the word "cult" as it is often applied to secret cults run by psychopaths where people are tortured or commit suicide with poisoned Kool-Aid or where they abuse children. In actuality, it was his comments that were controlling. He had behaved as if *he* were a cult leader telling a member what she was doing and disparaging her freedom to choose. She said his disparagement stopped her for a moment, but she realized that his nonsense had nothing to do with reality and went to the workshop. Nothing stopped her from acting to improve her situation and to gain mutual support.

Only you know who you are and where you are headed. In knowing this, you know that there isn't anyone who can influence you by telling you what you are or by implying that what you want to do is not good for you. You are capable of caring for yourself, researching and gathering the information you need, talking to specialists and professionals when you choose, tuning in to your intuition, and making wise choices.

This week, and for weeks to come, you will be more and more able to meet your needs and so improve your situation and so improve your life.

My Notes: From Week 33

Week 34

Your Affirmation: I do something toward my goals every day.

Your Message Each step, no matter how small, can lead you to your goal. Remind yourself daily what your goals are and remain positive that you can accomplish them. Every journey began with one step. Every garment began with one stitch. Sew—sow—your future garment, your future garden. Start with one seed you cherish and nurture—one idea that you want to bring to fruition. Think about it every day, and then do one small gesture to help it grow. Choose your "seeds" wisely—those of intrinsic value. Joy, friendship, artistic expression, and connection to others—these are worthy of your time on this planet.

What fits within your goals could be anything. That is to say, if connection to others were your goal, then anything from starting a small business community of entrepreneurs to support each other, to volunteering to teach reading to those who missed this education, would all be ways to build your connection to others. Even taking a class in a field of your interest or joining a hiking group would bring you an opportunity to build connections to others. Anything you choose to do to build connections may also meet other goals of intrinsic value.

As you explore your opportunities and take steps toward your goals you will be learning more about yourself and so will be developing awareness of just how able you are. Sometimes it seems like a good idea to wait to see what you feel like doing, and when there is no real feeling to do something, to wait a little longer. In fact, life usually works the other way around. First, one does, and then one feels.

As you act each day this week and in weeks to come with determination and focus to achieve your goals, your amazement at how much you can discover to love about yourself will grow. Joy will replace any self-doubt. You will trust yourself all the more, and all the positive affirmations you have practiced will provide you with fruits of self-knowledge, confidence, and satisfaction.

My Notes: From Week 34

Week 35

Your Affirmation: My creativity can never run out. Inspiration awaits me.

Your Message Your creativity comes from within you, and no one can take that away from you. Be open to all possibilities and your inspiration can be unlimited. Sometimes a moment of relaxation gives us the glimpse of this unending wellspring of creativity that lies within each of us. Daydreaming can unlock doors to new ideas, and inspire us to build something, create something, or try something we've never tried before. It is the very act of doing that reveals our boundless creativity. One small step and you find a window to new inspiration!

How reassuring it is to know that creativity never runs out. Creativity doesn't discriminate by race or age. Creativity is the ability to transcend our usual view of life and our approaches to solving problems or expressing our thoughts and feelings. This transcendence moves us to bring something new into being, be it an idea, an artistic expression, or a completely new way to sell a product. With creativity, we are inspired to see something in a new way and to fulfill its expression.

If you choose to explore your creativity, here is a way to begin. In quiet moments as you awaken in the morning, when the usual patterns of thought and beliefs are not yet barriers to inspiration and your imagination is active, write down your thoughts, dreams, hopes, and desires and later read what you have written. You may find inspiration more often than you might have thought.

This week and in weeks to come, allow yourself to enjoy and appreciate your unlimited creativity.

My Notes: From Week 35

Week 36

Your Affirmation: I am aligned with the creative force especially when I discover a creative solution to a problem.

Your Message Your mind and spirit tap into a greater consciousness when you seek a solution to a problem. When you carefully articulate the problem by describing it in detail, even possibly writing it down, an answer or a step toward finding the answer will come to you. Scientists and geniuses for centuries have acknowledged this greater creative force, and this wisdom is available to all. By clearly defining the problem, and asking for the solution, you will be given an answer. You are aligned with the noblest and highest of creative forces as you seek and find.

You may talk with many people and research many possible courses of action but as the answers come to you even sometimes in surprising ways, you feel their rightness. For instance, a woman told me that she had wrestled in her mind over a choice she had to make. She finally decided to say yes to an opportunity, even while she wondered if the choice would be worth the expense of her time and money and really benefit her. However, when she fully committed to saying yes by paying some necessary expenses, she felt as though a great weight had been lifted from her shoulders. She said it was hard to describe, but that she felt so relaxed and somehow uplifted, that she knew she had made the right decision.

If she were a student of eastern philosophy, she might have said, "I felt as though I were centered and in the Tao." If Christian, she might have said the Holy Spirit had come to her. In any case, she was aligned with the creative force moving her toward a solution to the problem confronting her.

Knowing that the creative force seeks expression within you and that seeking solutions to problems taps into that force, reinforces an optimistic and growth-oriented perspective that will serve you well in overcoming any difficulty in the coming week and in weeks to come.

My Notes: From Week 36

Week 37

Your Affirmation: I affirm my connection to the Divine Creative Force when I acknowledge my insights and inspirations.

Your Message When you look back on fortuitous decisions, and wise choices of the past, you can see a greater power at work. These are golden moments to recognize and affirm as connections to that great Divine Force that moves each of us forward. When awaking from a dream that delivers invaluable messages of guidance, you can vividly recall how connected you are to this higher power. By affirming these gifts of insight and inspiration, you affirm that you are connected at all times to a great, creative, guiding force. You can draw upon this power at any time you are in a highly alive and calm state.

As you care for yourself and trust yourself your trust in this connection grows. You attend to it, affirm it, and stay open to it. You note your dreams and follow your inspirations. You take comfort in the knowledge that creativity and inspiration are available to you and that as you use your gifts and talents you are becoming more and more who you were meant to be and more and more aligned with and even protected by the Divine Force.

This week and in weeks to come your life, your awareness, and your acknowledgement of your insights and inspirations affirm your connection to the Divine Creative Force. You are then never alone.

My Notes: From Week 37

Week 38

Your Affirmation: I choose to do what is best and right for my highest self, no matter how negatively I've been defined.

Your Message You may choose to make your own decisions, to be true to yourself in your choices, to decide what you want, and to be responsible for your own actions. You have this life to live in which to fulfill your true calling. It is never too late to choose for yourself a path of greatest good and contribution to your soul. Your highest self does not track time; it only lives in the moment.

All moments are valuable. The past exists nowhere in time or space. As you choose your path and how you will use your time in the present, you are actively creating an increasingly more satisfying future. You are also dissolving the imprint and impact of any verbal abuse you've heard. Any negative definition of who you are by anyone in any time or place has no meaning or reality. While you may have been the target, like a drive-by shooting, the comments were not your fault.

You are infinitely more deserving of love and care than any negative comments would say. They are simply little synapses that flew out of someone's mind. They are less meaningful than the chirping of a bird. Knowing this you are wiser and stronger each day. Knowing this you can choose to do what is best and right for your highest self this week and in the weeks to come.

My Notes: From Week 38

Week 39

Your Affirmation: I am in charge of myself; no one is in charge of me.

Your Message Every decision you make is truly your choice, and only your choice. When you think you have no options, you may choose to seek outside counsel. Trust your intuition, and if you do not get the information you need, keep looking for the answers. Ultimately, every action you take toward goals that are in keeping with your highest purpose will ultimately bring you satisfaction and fulfillment. And since no one is in charge of you, decisions and actions that you take are solely yours. The power to choose is within your hands, and it is a great power indeed. You always have a choice. No matter what you chose yesterday, you can choose something different today.

Make your own decisions. Be true to yourself in your choices. Decide what you want for your greatest good in keeping with your highest purpose and then begin choosing the steps you will take to achieve your goals. Whatever you choose, although it may take time to achieve, the journey will reveal the wisdom of your actions. If some choices do not bring you the results you seek, you may choose a different direction. It is as if life is an actual journey through mountains and valleys and across plains. This week and in weeks to come, as you exercise your freedom to choose, knowing that you are in charge of yourself, you will make your own path toward your highest purpose.

My Notes: From Week 39

Week 40

Your Affirmation: As I make wise choices in the present, I have future success.

Your Message A small decision—to improve, to create, to affirm, to seek, to strengthen—in this moment will create its own ripple effect, reaching out to the dawn of the next day and beyond. These small waves circle back to embrace you and carry you to the next positive step. This is the essence of success—to achieve small things that become changes to be celebrated, successes that empower. Today you can improve something, create something joyful, affirm health, seek enlightenment, and strengthen self.

The present you have now is the outcome of the past. If your trust has been betrayed by the assault of verbal abuse, whether in childhood or in an adult relationship, do not blame yourself but consider it one of life's adversities that leads to wisdom. Some people, like a wolf in sheep's clothing, or a person disguised as a parent, indulge in verbally abusive crazy talk. Your overcoming the influence of verbal abuse, making the small decisions that lead to success, creating your own future aligned with your highest purpose, all deepen your wisdom. Your life then lends strength and wisdom to others that they might through your example attain victory over verbal abuse.

This week and in the weeks to come your wise choices in the present bring you greater future success.

My Notes: From Week 40

Week 41

Your Affirmation: I seek success and successes increase my confidence.

Your Message Like bricks that are carefully laid to build a solid structure, successes are visible and tangible results that construct a solid foundation for esteem. Just as a brick fireplace and chimney can hold fire and yield light and warmth, so too do successful accomplishments become a structure within that gives strength to your very existence. This confidence can yield light and warmth in the world, and is your right.

Looking back in time at your successes awakens the feeling of accomplishment that passed through you with each achievement. To recall and savor these moments in a quiet time awakens their energy and can remind you of just who you are. All you achieved was not by accident, nor by pure luck, nor by a preordained destiny but by your actions, intentions and aspirations. You achieved all.

Success comes in many forms. It may be overcoming a fear, seeing a child comforted by your embrace, leaving a difficult relationship, graduating with a great degree or finding a job you like. It can be any way you have reached for something you didn't have, or let go of something you didn't want and so accomplished your goal. As you bask in the feeling of success, the desire to seek future success is lit like a new star on your horizon. As you seek success this week and in weeks to come, your confidence increases.

My Notes: From Week 41

Week 42

Your Affirmation: I appreciate the great miracle of my existence.

Your Message Though the incessant demands of day-to-day existence and the need to respond to the world can suspend your sense of the miraculous, each and every moment you are alive is truly a moment filled with miracles. Your body and mind are actively engaged in living, and the world around you is changed by your very presence. You were born into this life and carry a life force that belongs to you and the universe. This connects you to all that is, and draws you forward on a path of existence. This is a miracle millions of years in the making. You are here, now, today.

The miraculous is found within and recognized in stillness through the power of contemplation. In quiet moments, you may experience it, "I am here now. I occupy a time and space in the universe. I exist here. It is a miracle." This awareness generates the deepest appreciation and knowledge that all of us now sharing this moment in time are connected. Each is also unique.

You are as essential to the universe as the universe is essential to your existence. With this understanding there is no doubt that collectively, no matter who we are, what we do, or where we are, we are united in a deep and divine purpose, that of ever-increasing awareness. While someone may have defined you as not who you are, let your appreciation of just who you actually are radiate from the center of your being. Let your appreciation be like a sun that shines on those who are kind and lift them up with your appreciation, even as you appreciate the great miracle of your own existence. Know that all you appreciate in them is but a reflection of what is within you.

This week and for weeks to come, pause often to appreciate the miracle of your existence.

My Notes: From Week 42

Week 43

Your Affirmation: I can be all I want to be in the healthy, peaceful space I create for myself.

Your Message Using all of the tools and affirmations has led you to this week, this affirmation. There is a path forward now that gives you the healthy and calm space you desire. You need simply remember to seek it, take small steps to achieve it, affirm your success in each moment of peace you achieve, and like the flower that always turns to the sun, continue to turn toward healthy and peaceful conditions, and bloom.

Though you may have tread dangerous paths and waited for storms to subside, meticulously clearing the way, your efforts, actions, and intentions have removed the many blocks from your path and they have become stepping-stones to the present moment. Along the way, you may have had to let go of beliefs that no longer served you and moved away from people who have been toxic to you. The more you have become yourself the more clearly you have seen others for who they are.

As you create an uninterrupted peaceful space for yourself, you have the time and energy to focus on what you really want for yourself. The space around you includes not only your immediate environment, but also the people and places within the orbit of your activities. So, as you create peace in your personal space far from assaults and attacks, whether it is a room of your own, or a home of your own, so also you create a world of your own far from toxic people and places.

This week and in weeks to come, in the calm and healthy environment you create, you find extra energy and extra time to envision your life ever more in keeping with your desires, goals, gifts, passions, and inclinations.

My Notes: From Week 43

Week 44

Your Affirmation: I depend on no one for my happiness and tranquility.

Your Message Happiness comes from within. You can't find it in things, nor can you find it in a person. It comes from being who you really are and finding meaning and purpose in your life. No doubt, you can enjoy things, for instance, a car that runs well and meets your needs. No doubt, you can enjoy the company of friends, but feeling happy and tranquil comes from meeting your needs, knowing you can depend upon yourself, and doing whatever it is that gives meaning and purpose to your life.

Just about everyone has emotional highs and lows, so happiness isn't a constant state. But happiness can be thought of as a general sense of satisfaction about your life. If you know what you are grateful for, if you stop to consider all that is good in your life, you can choose to be happy.

Tranquility might be thought of as the opposite of worry and anxiety. Worry and anxiety usually exist where abuse has set limitations upon your freedom to live your life in the most fulfilling way. You are free to define yourself, your motives, preferences, intentions, actions, and needs. If you are free from the assaults of verbal abuse, other people's definitions of you, anxiety over the past will fade. The path to freedom may be long, for instance, if you must have contact with an abuser because of custody or business arrangements. However, the goal of freedom is universal among people everywhere, and this freedom will be yours. And, happiness and tranquility will be yours.

This week and for weeks to come, remind yourself that you can depend upon yourself, over all others, to find happiness in your life and the tranquility that comes with knowing that you do your best in keeping with your highest good.

My Notes: From Week 44

Week 45

Your Affirmation: If I find myself thinking of the past, I will stop myself and say "erase!" and will focus on something else.

Your Message You did not make anyone define you. You are not the cause of any abuse you suffered. Neither are you responsible for another person's behavior. If you find yourself going over and over an incident that hurt you, stop. Say "erase!" and focus on anything in front of you. Here are some examples of how to focus on something in the present. How many buttons are on my remote? How many keys are on my laptop? What is on my to-do list?

You are free in the present moment to think of anything you choose to think of. You are free to direct your mind. You will never again need to think of how to say things so the abuser hears you (or would have heard you), or how to explain yourself (or should have explained yourself). Ordinary people who are not abusive may say something unkind, but they apologize. Abusers don't. Abuse has nothing to do with you. It is simply directed at you.

Your time is yours. You can choose to spend this resource in a positive way. You may resolve never to consume your time and energy with negative thoughts that accomplish nothing. Recall your resolve to use your time and energy to act on your own behalf. Likewise if you find that you are trying to understand how the abuser could possibly think, for example, you are too sensitive, don't care, want to fight, and so forth, say "erase!" and focus on whatever is in front of you. After all, those who say these things are describing themselves.

Even if, through withholding responses and communications, you were defined as nonexistent, you now have the power to erase those experiences and to focus on the present.

I have seen both women and men who experience the rejection of withholding and criticism feel that they are not good enough. Consequently, they often try to do more and achieve more. Many regularly change careers, hobbies, occupations and avocations. Often they aren't even aware that their changed interest is mostly about trying to get acceptance from the rejecting abuser.

A man told me how he started various businesses, but never stayed with any since none, he now realized, brought him approval from his father. He said, "I started three different businesses, got a postgraduate degree, and even paid cash for a new car, but, somehow, my dad always brought me down, finding something to criticize. And when he couldn't find anything, which was mostly the case, he made something up, like my best employee was about to quit and what was the matter with me for hiring such a qualified guy, implying that if the employee were less qualified he would have stayed. Or the whole market was about to disappear for my products, so how could I be so stupid."

A woman told me how she took up various arts and, although she was a good guitarist, then a painter, then a jewelry designer, and then an interior decorator, she had not stayed with any pursuit long enough to be really successful. As soon as she had an award, a blue ribbon, or other commendation, her abuser would discount it as nothing, and she would, without really considering her motives, try something new.

This will never happen to you because you can choose to congratulate yourself on your achievements. You have the power.

My Notes: From Week 45

Week 46

Your Affirmation: I am aware of my thoughts and always change negative ones to positive ones.

Your Message Sometimes thoughts can be so quiet, so "in the background," that we can miss the fact that they just whizzed by. Some of the most negative thoughts can be the most difficult to recognize. By paying attention to your inner voice, choosing frequent quiet moments to listen in, you can discover and weed out the negative thoughts. In their place, you can reload with a positive affirmation. This is like weeding a garden: You must pull up the negative thoughts—the weeds—as they spring up. You can plant increasingly positive thoughts and affirmations, to build a garden of abundance that provides endless joy to your spirit. Like weeds, small negative thoughts can sprout up without notice out of long-buried seeds. Each day is an opportunity to remove them once and for all. Eventually, there will be no negative seeds left buried or falling into your mental garden.

Long-buried seeds that sprout negative thoughts can be spotted even as they begin to take root. They can be found buried even before they sprout into consciousness. They lie under negative, restrictive, or clearly irrational feelings—the kinds that lead one to wonder, "Why do I feel that way?" If this question arises, it is time to look back at your earliest memories and then to ask, "What might I have heard or seen or experienced that would lead me to feel this way?"

An answer may come to you such as, "When I was little I thought this because I heard . . ." Now, in the light of your new awareness, it is not difficult to discard a negative thought and with it, the negative feeling it generated.

This week and in weeks to come, your garden of positive thoughts will grow, as will your awareness and happiness.

My Notes: From Week 46

Week 47

Your Affirmation: My personal strength and willpower are always with me.

Your Message Your inner strength and the power of your will might not be evident in ordinary circumstances. But, when you face a challenge, knowing that you have great strength to heal and to apply to the tasks at hand can enhance your confidence and determination. Many people have an inner strength that they might not have imagined. It is when we are called upon to face a challenge that we discover our capabilities and so we trust ourselves.

Your strength originates with your being able to love yourself, to be kind and accepting of yourself. Your willpower is exercised in your determination to live your life according to your values, to never neglect yourself, to always care for yourself.

If a shadow crosses your path on the journey of your life, it is dispelled by the light of your awareness and the power you have to dissolve it. You know that your strength flows through your will and that you exercise your will to confront, to act, to do what is necessary to overcome any difficulty. Yet, at no time will you expect perfection of yourself nor will you judge yourself.

Your willpower serves you well as you go about your life and are conscious this week and in weeks to come that, with willpower, you can act consciously for your own good and the good of all in even the smallest thing.

My Notes: From Week 47

Week 48

Your Affirmation: Time is my resource and I will use it wisely.

Your Message You have a resource that is yours and yours alone. It is time. You alone can choose how to use that resource. You may choose to give time to your family, your career, yourself, or anything at all. It is precious and it can be used only in the present. By using it wisely, you can place your trust in the future. Your future is your own unfolding, a becoming of who you really are, and an unfolding of your own uniqueness.

Since time is your resource, you can allocate it, schedule it, share it, and plan how to use it. With this in mind, you may choose to be in the present moment to keep track of not only what is happening within and around you, but also how you are using your precious resource, time. Just as in planning a financial budget, the first step in creating your own "time budget" is to track how you are spending, not your money, but your time!

Consider the past thirty days. Once you know how you've spent your time, decide how you want to use it in the coming month. Please be sure to include time for fun in your time budget. A time budget should be flexible so you can adjust it to your priorities.

You can choose to use your time budget as a guide to make sure that you don't forget your priorities, for instance, time for: breakfast, lunch, dinner, sleep, exercise, recovery processes, therapies, reading, supportive friends, work, and so forth.

How you use your time is your own choice. In choosing, it is important to ask yourself if anyone currently or in the past has taken your time, controlled your time, or used your time to your own detriment. Have you given up your time to avoid confrontation, to keep the peace, to be nice, to avoid saying no to unreasonable demands?

With your ever-increasing clarity and personal power, you treasure your time, all the time. This week and in weeks to come your time will be a resource you spend for your highest good.

My Notes: From Week 48

Week 49

Your Affirmation: This week, I will gift myself with time that I will use to do something just for me.

Your Message It may seem like a riddle: What do we all have, always, yet it can run but never get anywhere else; some people seem to have more of it on their hands, and yet it belongs to each of us equally? Time. This is the great miracle, this very moment at which everything can change. You need only to choose this moment to do something for you, to demonstrate to the universe that you are worth this pause, this minute, this gift of tranquil time. Setting aside some time to do something just for you is as natural as a leaf that turns to capture the sun. This is nurturing, important, and affirming. You are acknowledging your power in those moments to sustain your spirit.

I give myself permission to let go of all concerns; after all, worry over anything not only does not change what I might have worried about but also steals time and energy from me. Since I replace all negative thoughts with positive ones, my time is spent in a positive atmosphere that I alone create. I surround myself with this optimistic aura. I dissolve all negative thoughts of needing to accomplish more with my time. This week and in weeks to come, I live in the knowledge that my time is mine and I take my time.

My Notes: From Week 49

Week 50

Your Affirmation: I protect myself for I am more valuable than diamonds or gold.

Your Message It is sometimes easier to protect a car or a child than it is to protect one's own self. We insure our jewelry and our homes and yet may ignore the very miracle that performs these actions—ourselves. Yet, each person is a far more glorious machine than any car, and each body houses a spirit that is far more important than worldly possessions. It is your right and your obligation to protect that incredible treasure called "you."

When words are used to diminish your value, or if you have allowed negativity to undermine your esteem the way termites will eat away at a home, then you must take immediate action to protect yourself from further harm. You can look inward and see the glimmer of hope, the shine of spirit, and the sparkle that is uniquely you. Then cherish the inner self, protect it, and imbue yourself with esteem. You are the jewel you wear.

Like a diamond with many facets, every aspect of your being will shine as it catches the spotlight of your awareness. Every aspect is protected and free to be. Your talents shine, your views are respected, and your thoughts are valued. All are sheltered by your ability to protect yourself from any who would diminish them. This week and in weeks to come you hold yourself in the arms of awareness, ever ready to keep yourself from harm's way.

My Notes: From Week 50

Week 51

Your Affirmation: I am as valuable as anyone and no one can diminish me.

Your Message When people who claim to love them hit people with verbal abuse they struggle to reconstitute themselves. But over and over their inner world, their very consciousness is slammed. If they are yelled at, their brain will record the assault like a physical blow. They are told that their motives are not their motives; their feelings are not what they are. They are even told what they want and need and should do.

One way to set a boundary is to imagine a fence, strong, sturdy, white posts and cross beams. You can see over and through the fence, lean on it for a conversation with friends, and grow your garden protected from foragers.

From your side of the fence, you are strong, healthy, vital, and valuable. You will not allow anyone to trespass onto your property and poison your land and what you have grown there. When someone tries to diminish you, and you let him or her onto your land with their poison because you believed them when they said they loved you, then you must push them back behind the fence. They cannot be allowed back into your spirit. You can rebuild and till the soil where they walked, and you can even converse with them over the fence. But now, you protect you with a boundary that does not allow their footfall, their words, or their actions to diminish any part of your property.

This week and in the weeks to come I build a fence around my mind and spirit, and like a one-way mirror I can see out but none can enter without my invitation. Diminishing and defining comments are deflected and, like drips from a broken drain, flow into the gutter from which they came.

My Notes: From Week 51

Week 52

Your Affirmation: I stay in the present moment so I don't worry about the future.

Your Message The only thing that is certain is change. For that reason, there is always some uncertainty. However, if you are focused in the present and do not dwell on the past you will be better able to act to take care of yourself and to respond in the best way to whatever comes up in the present moment.

In the same way, worrying about the future is unproductive. We can't change the past, although we can view it in a different way, as a journey, for instance. And, we can't predict the future; we can only deal with the present and if we do our best in the present, the future will unfold, as it should.

Ultimately it is faith in yourself and providence that dissolves all worries. And even with little faith in yourself you might know that what you might worry about may never even happen. Worry is wasted time and energy.

Being mindful, noticing what you are thinking about, and directing your thoughts, can help. If you practiced mindfulness in Week 46, you can apply this practice to your concerns by reminding yourself that, whatever the future brings, you are up for it.

You have completed a year. Your determination, focus, and dedication to yourself have brought change. Now, if you go to Week 1 and see your notes, you will not only be looking at your progress, but experiencing it from within.

Beginning a second year of affirmations will bring more amazing change into your life, into your consciousness, and into the world.

Congratulations.

My Notes: From Week 52

Index

About the Author

Founder of the Evans Interpersonal Communications Institute, now, EICI, Inc.; Patricia Evans has single-handedly brought the subject of verbal abuse to the forefront of American consciousness. *Newsweek* described her first book, *The Verbally Abusive Relationship*, as "groundbreaking." Her other bestselling books explain other forms of control, what is wrong with abusers, and how to wake them up.

Evans has spoken out on the devastating effect of verbal abuse, a secret form of control, on twenty national television programs, including *The Oprah Winfrey Show* and CNN. She has also given informational interviews on hundreds of radio shows. With an ever-increasing stream of e-mails and calls, she has heard from more than thirty thousand people, mostly women in verbally abusive relationships. Evans has presented and conducted workshops throughout the United States, Canada, and Australia. She also presented in Madrid to the first Commission for the Investigation of Violence Against Women.

In private phone consultations, Patricia Evans has consulted to over a thousand people, helping both targets and perpetrators of verbal abuse to not only understand what has happened in their relationships, but also to know why people indulge in verbal abuse, what to do about it, and how to recover.

On her website, *www.verbalabuse.com,* you will find more information about verbal abuse, her books, and the first and only mini-documentary on verbal abuse as well as an online support group, where more than six thousand women have registered.

Born and raised in the San Francisco Bay Area, when Evans completed her university degree in Living Systems Theory and entered graduate school, she discovered that there were no degrees in her area of interest—none that applied Living Systems Theory to interpersonal communications. With the suggestion and encouragement of philosophy professor Carl H. Putz, PhD (1940–2010), she wrote her first book and has continued writing ever since.

Getting Where Women Really Belong

- Trying to lose the losers you've been dating?
- Striving to find the time to be a doting mother, dedicated employee, and still be a hot piece of you-know-what in the bedroom?
- Been in a comfortable relationship that's becoming, well, too comfortable?

Don't despair! Visit the Jane on Top blog—your new source for information (and commiseration) on all things relationships, sex, and the juggling act that is being a modern gal.

Sign up for our newsletter at

www.adamsmedia.com/blog/relationships

and download a **Month-ful of Happiness!**

That's 30 days of free tips guaranteed to lift your mood!